Introduction

Every food business uses, processes and sells food in different ways. However, the general issues and key principles remain the same, whatever the style of the operation. *Food Safety for Supervisors* gives you essential information and advice that is applicable wherever food is handled. Use the book to improve your understanding of the underlying principles of food safety then to refine those principles to good practice in your own workplace.

Food Safety for Supervisors is divided into five parts.

Part 1 considers potential hazards – microbial, physical, chemical and allergenic – that are commonly associated with food and the impact they may have on health. It also revises and builds upon basic level microbiology, the prevention of food-borne illnesses and food spoilage.

Part 2 covers in detail how hazards are controlled. After considering how contamination may be prevented, following chapters outline potential hazards to be found in various areas of food handling and consider specific control measures and good practice.

The majority of food businesses have a legal obligation to put in place and maintain a permanent procedure based on Hazard Analysis Critical Control Point (HACCP) principles so **Part 3** considers conventional HACCP and *Safer Food, Better Business* – the tool developed by the Food Standards Agency to help small businesses to comply with the requirement for a documented food safety management system.

Informed and competent managers and supervisors are fundamental to food safety. **Part 4** focuses on aspects of the management process itself and the supervisor's role. Guidance is given on monitoring and control methods and quality assurance and the supervisor's role in food safety training and possible involvement in an investigation of an outbreak of food-borne illness.

Part 5 concentrates on UK food safety legislation. However, as most food legislation now originates from the European Union the food safety principles covered in this part are relevant to most countries. Food law, as with any law, is complex and often looked upon as confusing. Supervisors are not expected to know all the fine details. However, they must have a general awareness of its main contents and requirements so that they can bring any potential problems or concerns directly to the attention of management. Part 5 is included for reference only.

Part 1

Potential hazards

Chapter 1
Introduction to food safety

Food safety is the absence of any risk of harm from food. Generally speaking, food safety describes the practice of managing food in such a way that the food is highly unlikely to cause any harmful effects, whether in the short term or long term, to anyone who consumes products that have been processed, stored or sold by the business. Food hygiene can be considered as the practical process of ensuring that food is fit to eat.

Brief review of definitions

Technical terms are explained in the Glossary, but some terms you will encounter in the book are included here as a quick reminder. You should already be familiar with the simple meaning of most of them.

Allergy/allergic reaction

A food allergy is an identifiable immunological response to food or food additives. The symptoms range from mild through to life threatening and vary from individual to individual. In the case of a severe food allergy, consuming even a tiny amount of food can be life-threatening.

Carrier

This is someone who is infected with a specific pathogen that can be passed on to other people. A healthy carrier carries the pathogen but does not develop any symptoms of the disease. A convalescent or incubatory carrier has suffered from the disease and is a carrier during the incubation period or during or after convalescence. The carrier state may be long term or short term.

Contamination

The transference of any objectionable or harmful substance or material to food. The contaminant may be microbial, physical, chemical or one that causes an allergic reaction

Food-borne disease

An illness caused by micro-organisms (e.g. bacteria, viruses) carried by food or water.

Only a small number of micro-organisms are needed and in contrast to food poisoning bacteria, the multiplication of disease-producing (pathogenic) organisms in the food is not an essential feature as the food merely acts as a vehicle. The interval between infection and the appearance of the first sign of symptoms (the incubation period) is usually several days or even weeks, unlike bacterial food poisoning where symptoms may develop within hours.

Food-borne illness

The general term for illnesses caused by eating contaminated food. Food poisoning and food-borne disease come under this general heading.

High-risk food –
ready-to-eat, high
protein, moist,
requires refrigeration

Food poisoning

An acute illness that usually develops rapidly after eating contaminated or poisonous food. The symptoms vary but often include abdominal pain, diarrhoea, vomiting and nausea. Food poisoning may be caused by:

- bacteria or their toxins
- chemicals
- metals
- poisonous fish
- poisonous plants.

Gastro-enteritis

An inflammation of the stomach and intestines that can cause diarrhoea, abdominal pain, nausea and vomiting.

High-risk food

Foods that, under favourable conditions, support the multiplication of pathogenic bacteria and are intended for consumption without further treatment that would destroy pathogens. Such foods are usually ready-to-eat, high protein, moist foods that require refrigeration. They include:

- cooked meats and cooked meat products, including gravy and stock
- milk, cream, custards
- eggs
- dairy products
- cooked poultry
- shellfish and other seafood
- cooked rice.

Incubation period

The interval between the infection of an individual and the appearance of the first sign or symptom of a disease.

Onset period

The period between consumption of contaminated food and the first signs of illness.

Pathogen

Disease-producing organisms such as the bacteria that cause food poisoning or food-borne disease

Hygiene in practice

Food hygiene is not just a matter of making food premises look clean. The activities involved include:

- protecting food against any type of contamination
- preventing any organism from multiplying to levels that put consumers' health at risk or result in food spoilage
- destroying any harmful bacteria in food or food premises
- removing contaminated food so that it cannot be used for human consumption.

The benefits of high standards of food hygiene

The public has a considerable interest in food safety and high expectations of those involved in the food business, but general confidence is sometimes shaken by food scares. It is, therefore, important that food businesses have high standards of food hygiene and that these are clear to everyone.

High standards help to create a good reputation for food businesses. In turn, this helps to:

- boost customer confidence
- increase business
- swell profits
- enhance staff morale and loyalty
- improve the standard and quality of the food
- reduce waste
- prevent food-borne illness.

The costs of poor standards of food hygiene

The costs of poor hygiene to a food business can be very high and can include:

- the loss of reputation leading to:
  - low morale
  - loss of business, possibly including valuable contracts
  - lower profits
- poor control of food leading to:
  - high levels of wastage
  - loss of production
  - spoilt food
  - pest infestation
  - food poisoning and food-borne disease
  - complaints
- higher costs resulting in:
  - high staff turnover
  - legal action and fines
  - civil action for compensation by people who have become ill
  - increase in insurance premiums
  - food wastage
  - closure of the business.

People employed in food businesses with poor hygiene standards may have to deal with:

- the loss of their jobs – either because of the closure of premises, or because of a loss of business
- becoming a long-term carrier of pathogenic organisms
- damaged personal reputations if their workplace is known to have poor hygiene standards
- the loss of overtime and bonuses.

The incidence of food poisoning

The last twenty years has seen a significant increase in the number of people suffering from food poisoning. In 1984 there were approximately 21,000 reported cases in England and Wales. This rose to a peak of just below 94,000 cases in 1998 falling to approximately 70,000 cases in 2004. However, this is considered to be far lower than the true figure as many people who are ill do not visit a doctor and are not included in the official statistics. It is estimated that reported cases are just the 'tip of the iceberg' and that many cases go unreported every year with an equivalent number of working days lost. The collection of reliable data is also complicated by whether or not food-borne diseases and viral food poisoning are included: they may produce similar symptoms, but may or may not have been carried by food.

Notified cases

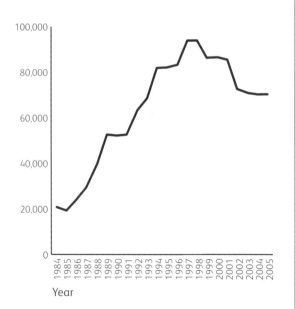

Year

Source: Health Protection Agency, Statutory Notifications
of Infectious Diseases (NOIDs)

There are many reasons proposed for the increase in food-borne illnesses including:

- more people eating out
- convenience foods being prepared incorrectly by the end user
- different types of food outlets selling more exotic foods
- a greater number of meals served at certain times – such as Christmas and weddings
- misuse of equipment – such as microwave ovens and refrigerators
- seasonal variations – for instance, in summer there may be:
  - higher ambient temperatures
  - overstocked refrigerators
  - people buying more prepared cold food such as cooked meat
  - holidays abroad
  - temporary staff in holiday resorts
  - food transported in vehicles with no refrigeration
  - barbecues.

The increase in food-borne illness may be linked to more people eating out

Chapter 2
Identifying hazards

There will always be food safety hazards, but they can be controlled if you understand how food becomes contaminated and how to prevent this from happening.

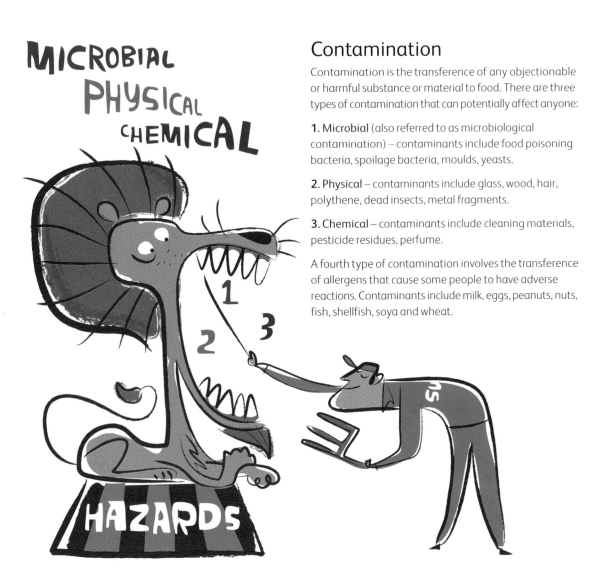

Contamination

Contamination is the transference of any objectionable or harmful substance or material to food. There are three types of contamination that can potentially affect anyone:

1. Microbial (also referred to as microbiological contamination) – contaminants include food poisoning bacteria, spoilage bacteria, moulds, yeasts.

2. Physical – contaminants include glass, wood, hair, polythene, dead insects, metal fragments.

3. Chemical – contaminants include cleaning materials, pesticide residues, perfume.

A fourth type of contamination involves the transference of allergens that cause some people to have adverse reactions. Contaminants include milk, eggs, peanuts, nuts, fish, shellfish, soya and wheat.

Microbial contamination

Microbial contamination is the presence in food of pathogenic micro-organisms including bacteria, viruses, moulds and yeasts

Bacteria

Bacteria are the most common form of microbial contamination and sources include:

Raw food

Bacteria are naturally present in the environment and in animal intestines, so raw food – including meat, shellfish, eggs, vegetables and untreated milk – may already carry pathogenic bacteria before it reaches your workplace. Raw meat and poultry may be contaminated with types of *Salmonella, Clostridia, Campylobacter* and *E. coli* O157 that have spread from the animal's intestines to the carcass during slaughter. Contact between carcasses and between different types of meat provides an ideal opportunity for bacteria to spread.

People

Careless handling during transport, manufacture, preparation and service may add bacteria to food or spread them between foods. Food poisoning bacteria can be transferred from raw to high-risk foods by food handlers' hands. The bacteria involved are usually *Staphylococci* from the nose, mouth, cuts and skin and *Salmonellae* from the bowel.

Equipment

Food-contact surfaces, utensils and equipment that have not been adequately cleaned and disinfected can harbour bacteria that may be passed on to food.

Air and dust

Air can carry millions of microscopic particles including pathogenic particles that can settle on food. Ventilation systems can circulate air-borne contaminants.

Soil

Unwashed fruit and vegetables can carry soil and bacteria that can contaminate food.

Pests

Food pests and other animals – rodents, birds, stored product pests, cockroaches, flies, cats and dogs – can spread bacteria to food.

Water

Inadequately treated water supplies and ineffective drainage systems can carry and spread bacteria.

Food waste

If it is not clearly identified, properly contained and disposed of on a regular basis, food waste can be used in error and/or attract pests – both of these situations can lead to the contamination of food.

Sources of bacteria include raw meat, hands and food-contact surfaces

Viruses

Viruses may be carried into food premises by food handlers or raw food such as vegetables or shellfish that have been in contact with sewage-polluted water.

Moulds

Mould spores are found in the atmosphere, on surfaces – especially damp ones such as walls – and on mouldy food. The growth rate of mould increases when food is stored at an incorrect temperature in high humidity and for longer than is recommended. Although some types of mould may not be harmful to health, the presence of mould is considered to be unacceptable and may result in prosecution because food contaminated with mould is unfit for human consumption. For information on mycotoxins (poisons produced by some moulds) *see* page 37.

Yeasts

Yeasts can multiply over a wide temperature range including temperatures below 0°C in some species. They prefer slightly acidic conditions (pH 4.0) and can multiply in foods with a high sugar content. Yeasts are used in the manufacture of bread and beer. Yeasts do not cause food poisoning, but several species cause food spoilage, especially in acidic foods that also have a high sugar content such as found in fruit, fruit juice, jam and wine.

Moulds grow when food is stored at incorrect temperatures

Yeasts can multiply in foods with a high sugar content

Physical contamination

Physical contamination is anything that falls into or onto food. The contamination may come from a variety of sources and can be introduced at any stage of food handling from 'farm to fork' – from growing, harvesting, slaughter, distribution, storage, processing, packing, delivering, displaying, through to the point of purchase or consumption by the consumer. Physical contamination can be harmful and unpleasant.

Sources of physical contamination include people, packaging material and machinery or equipment

Sources of physical contamination include:

- **people** – hair, fingernails, jewellery, buttons, plasters, sweet papers, cigarettes, pens

- **packaging materials** – cardboard, polythene, string, plastic, wood, staples

- **machinery/equipment** – bolts, nuts, screws, electrical fittings, rust, fragments (metal, plastic, fabric) from conveyors, grease and oil

- **premises** – glass (from windows, lighting, equipment), flakes of paint from walls, rust from pipe-work

- **pests** – fur, feathers, droppings, eggs, larvae, dead bodies

- **environment** – dust, dirt (in the air, from equipment, from rubbish)

- **raw materials** – hide, bone (from meat), feathers (from poultry), shells (from eggs and nuts), dirt, stones, leaves, stalks (from fruit and vegetables).

Chemical contamination

Chemical contamination may occur if:

- raw food is treated with excessive levels of pesticide, preservative or mould inhibitor
- veterinary drugs (such as antibiotics) are misused during the rearing of animals
- cleaning chemicals are misused or incorrectly stored
- food additives are used beyond permitted levels
- food handlers use perfume, scented soap, aftershave or other grooming products
- there is a chemical reaction between a metal and an acidic food.

For information on possible symptoms as a result of chemical food poisoning *see* page 34.

Chemical contamination can be caused by pesticide residues or cleaning chemicals

Food allergy

A food that is perfectly safe for one person to eat may be extremely hazardous to another. Some people experience allergic reactions to certain foods – reactions that can range from mild to life threatening. It is, therefore, vitally important that all people who prepare or handle food, in the context of catering, manufacturing or retailing, are fully aware of the foods that may be allergenic and what precautions need to be taken to ensure that contamination does not occur.

A food allergy is an identifiable immunological response to food or food additives. Some symptoms, such as vomiting and diarrhoea, are similar to those of food poisoning. However, food allergies should not be confused with any food-borne illness. Symptoms range from a mild flushing of the skin, or swelling of the throat and mouth, both of which can be treated with an oral medication (for example, antihistamine), to collapse and unconsciousness, where an adrenaline injection should be given as soon as possible and urgent medical help must be sought. In an extreme attack, an individual may have an anaphylactic shock (dramatic fall in blood pressure leading to a rapid loss of consciousness), which can be life threatening.

Foods known to cause allergic reactions include milk, eggs and peanuts

Any food can cause a food allergy. However, EU legislation clearly identifies 14 foods that must be mentioned on food labels if they are used as ingredients in pre-packed foods.

The 14 foods are:

- celery
- cereals containing gluten (wheat, barley, rye and oats)
- crustaceans (for example: lobster and crab)
- eggs
- fish
- lupin
- milk
- molluscs (for example: mussels and oysters)
- mustard
- nuts (for example almonds, Brazil nuts, cashews, hazelnuts, pecans, pistachios, macadamia nuts and walnuts)
- peanuts (also called groundnuts)
- sesame seeds
- soybeans (sometimes called soya)
- sulphur dioxide and sulphites (preservatives used on some foods and drinks) at levels above 10mg per kg or per litre).

Most of these foods are easy to identify and require no further explanation. However, some of them such as sesame seeds, soya and lupin are less obvious. Sesame seeds are often used in bread and breadsticks, sesame paste (tahini) is used in Greek and Turkish dishes including humous and sesame oil is used for cooking or in dressings. Soya comes in different forms, for example, tofu (or bean curd), soya flour, textured soya protein, soya milk, and is found in a wide range of foods including ice cream, sauces, desserts, meat products and vegetarian products such as 'veggie' burgers. Lupin seeds (also called lupin beans) can be used as an alternative ingredient to soya in some food products, for example, in vegetarian sausages, lupin tofu, lupin flour and lupin milk.

Allergic reactions

Most common symptoms include:

- coughing
- dry, itchy throat and tongue
- itchy skin or rash
- nausea and feeling bloated
- diarrhoea and/or vomiting
- wheezing and shortness of breath
- swelling of the lips and throat
- runny or blocked nose
- sore, red and itchy eyes.

Severe allergic reactions (anaphylaxis) can include symptoms in different parts of the body at the same time:

- rashes
- swelling of the lips and throat
- difficulty breathing
- rapid fall in blood pressure
- loss of consciousness.

(Source: Foods Standards Agency – www.eatwell.gov.uk)

Outline of food hazards

These charts give an at-a-glance guide to hazards and their consequences.

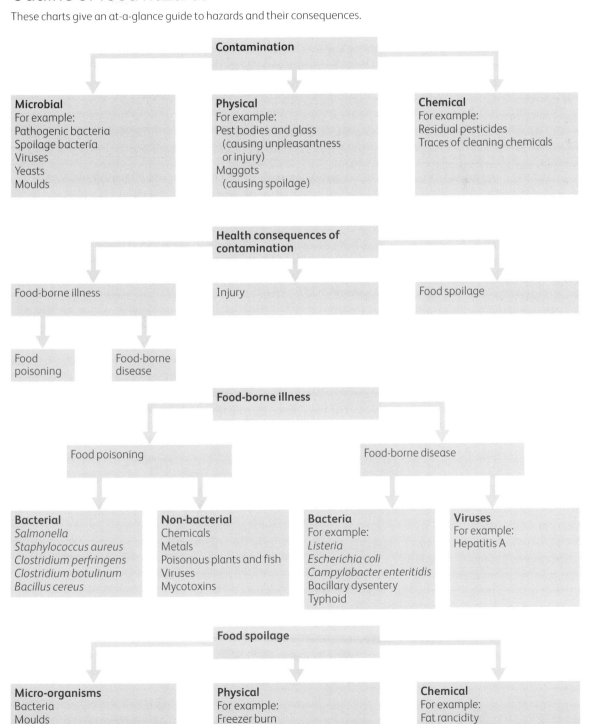

Contamination

Microbial
For example:
Pathogenic bacteria
Spoilage bacteria
Viruses
Yeasts
Moulds

Physical
For example:
Pest bodies and glass
 (causing unpleasantness
 or injury)
Maggots
 (causing spoilage)

Chemical
For example:
Residual pesticides
Traces of cleaning chemicals

Health consequences of contamination

Food-borne illness

Injury

Food spoilage

Food poisoning

Food-borne disease

Food-borne illness

Food poisoning

Food-borne disease

Bacterial
Salmonella
Staphylococcus aureus
Clostridium perfringens
Clostridium botulinum
Bacillus cereus

Non-bacterial
Chemicals
Metals
Poisonous plants and fish
Viruses
Mycotoxins

Bacteria
For example:
Listeria
Escherichia coli
Campylobacter enteritidis
Bacillary dysentery
Typhoid

Viruses
For example:
Hepatitis A

Food spoilage

Micro-organisms
Bacteria
Moulds
Yeasts

Physical
For example:
Freezer burn
Insect infestation

Chemical
For example:
Fat rancidity
Enzyme activity

Chapter 3
Microbiology

Microbiology involves the study of micro-organisms that are generally too small to be seen without a microscope and include bacteria, moulds and yeasts. A thorough understanding of microbes, in particular bacteria, is important at all stages of food production 'from farm to fork'.

Types of bacteria

Bacteria can be found everywhere – on people, animals and food and in soil and water. Their presence can only be confirmed with the aid of a microscope unless they have formed slime, for instance on meat, or are present in large numbers in a colony.

Most bacteria are harmless and some are used to our advantage – for instance, in the manufacture of yoghurt and cheese. However, two categories of bacteria create major problems in the food industry. They are spoilage bacteria and pathogenic bacteria.

Spoilage bacteria

These bacteria break down protein, causing spoilage or putrefaction that may be detectable by smell, but do not usually cause food poisoning. There is more information about spoilage in Chapter 7.

Pathogenic bacteria

These bacteria are responsible for causing illness especially when large numbers of them are present in the food. They rarely alter the appearance, taste or smell of food. There is more information about these bacteria in Chapter 4.

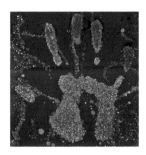

The presence of bacteria is not usually evident – here they can be seen as colonies

Characteristics of bacteria

Bacteria are measured in micrometers (or microns) expressed as µm. One µm equals one thousandth of a millimetre. A bacterium of the *Salmonella* family may be just 3µm long. Bacteria have a variety of shapes:

- Cocci are spherical. Some, such as *Streptococcus faecalis*, form chains. Others, such as *Staphylococcus aureus*, form a cluster that looks a little like a bunch of grapes.
- Bacilli, such as the *Salmonella* species, are rod-shaped.
- Spirochaetes, such as *Leptospira interrogans*, which can cause Weil's disease in humans, are spiral-shaped.
- Vibrio, such as *Vibrio cholerae*, are comma-shaped.

Reproduction – binary fission

Bacteria multiply by the process of binary fission – non-sexually dividing in two. The correct conditions must be available before this can happen (for example, a suitable supply of nutrients or an acceptable temperature). Following division, each grows to maturity and itself divides. The time between each division (the generation time) varies but is on average 10 to 20 minutes. The false colour electron micrograph shown below at a magnification x 57,000 shows a *Staphylococcus aureus* bacterium in the process of cell division. The cell walls (red) and the genetic material (purple) are visible. When binary fission is complete, there will be two, separate, identical bacteria.

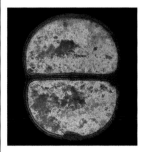

Bacteria multiply by the process of binary fission

Spores

When conditions start to deteriorate, for example high temperature, dehydration or the presence of disinfectants, most bacteria die. However, two groups of bacteria, *Bacilli* and *Clostridia*, can produce spores capable of surviving these adverse conditions. The living vegetative cell forms a hard cell-like structure inside itself that contains all the necessary material to continue life once conditions improve. In the false-coloured electron micrograph shown below at a magnification x 20,000 a *Clostridium perfringens* bacterium is towards the end of spore formation. The spore, visible in the lower part of the bacterium, is shown in green with a red membrane. Once the spore is completely formed the rest of the vegetative cell breaks down leaving the spore that can remain viable in this state for long periods – maybe for years. When conditions improve, the spore absorbs moisture, expands and splits or 'germinates' to produce a new vegetative cell that can now multiply normally by binary fission. In addition to *Clostridium perfringens* other spore-forming bacteria that can cause problems in the food industry are *Clostridium botulinum* and *Bacillus cereus*.

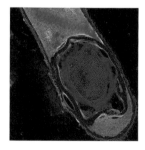

Clostridium perfringens

Toxins

Some bacteria produce poisonous substances, called toxins, in food. Toxins that cause gastro-enteritis are referred to as enterotoxins. This general term covers two specific types of toxin:

1. Exotoxins – produced during the multiplication of bacteria in food or as waste products (in the same way that we produce waste following digestion).

2. Endotoxins – which form part of the cell wall and are released on the death of the bacteria.

Exotoxins can be heat resistant and, therefore, survive cooking (for example, the toxin produced by *Staphylococcus aureus*). The bacteria will be killed by the cooking process, but the toxin will remain and can still cause illness. There are also toxins that affect the central nervous system and may cause death. *Clostridium botulinum* produces such a toxin – a neurotoxin.

Conditions required for multiplication

Nutrients

Bacteria need similar nutrients to humans – high-protein foods, such as meat, meat products, poultry, eggs, milk, milk products and seafood. Increasing salt, sugar, acid or fat levels will reduce the ability for bacteria to multiply to the point where growth will eventually be prevented altogether – for example in the curing of meats, jam making and pickling.

Bacteria thrive on high protein foods

Increasing salt, sugar and acid levels will restrict bacterial multiplication

Temperature

Bacteria multiply at temperatures between 5°C and 63°C, the range known as the danger zone. Bacteria multiply more slowly if it is cold and become dormant in very cold conditions. At temperatures above 63°C most food poisoning bacteria die or, if they can, create spores.

The average ideal temperature for rapid bacterial multiplication is 37°C. However, different bacteria multiply at different maximum and minimum temperatures and each bacterium has an optimum temperature for reproduction.

Bacteria can be divided into four main groups with the following optimum multiplication temperatures:

1. Psychrophiles – 10°C (range -5–20°C) – examples include both bacteria and moulds that cause spoilage in refrigerated foods.

2. Psychrotrophs – 20°C (range 0–35°C) – examples include *Listeria monocytogenes* and many spoilage bacteria.

3. Mesophiles – 35°C (range 10–50°C) – examples include most common pathogens, such as *Salmonella*, *Staphylococcus aureus*, *Campylobacter* species.

4. Thermophiles – 50°C (range 40–80°C) – examples include bacteria that cause spoilage in canned foods.

The average ideal temperature for bacterial multiplication is 37°C

Time

All bacteria need time to multiply in the right conditions. Under optimum conditions bacteria can divide into two every 10 to 20 minutes. Given a generation time of 15 minutes a typical bacterial load (number of bacteria) of 10,000 could reach potential food poisoning levels within 90 minutes (640,000) and certainly within 120 minutes (2,560,000). The number of *Salmonella* organisms needed to cause illness (the infective dose) is usually 100,000 per gram of food and for *Clostridium perfringens* 1,000,000 per gram of food.

Bacteria need time, moisture and a pH of 6–8

Moisture (a_w)

Bacteria need moisture to stay alive. Dry products are, therefore, unsuitable for bacterial multiplication, but spore forming bacteria can survive dehydration. The moisture available to bacteria from food is usually measured as water activity, expressed as a_w. The a_w of pure water is 1.00, and bacteria generally need 0.95 or above to stay active. The a_w of most high protein foods range from 0.97 to 0.99, which is ideal for pathogenic bacteria. Breads have a_w levels around 0.94 and 0.96, which is low for most bacteria but suitable for mould growth. Jam has an a_w of approximately 0.75, which is generally too low for bacterial multiplication and also for most moulds and yeasts, too. Lowering a_w can be used to preserve food. In the case of jam, a high sugar concentration binds water and lowers the a_w level. In the case of flours (a_w 0.65 to 0.85) cereals are dried to an appropriate moisture level to achieve a stable product with a long shelf life in dry ambient conditions.

pH

The pH scale measures how acid or alkaline a substance is. A pH value of 7 is neutral – water is neutral. Acidic foods have a pH below 7, while alkaline foods have a pH above 7. Bacteria prefer a pH of 6 to 8 and many foods fall within this range. Bacteria generally will not multiply below pH 4.5. Fruit juices fall into this category – orange and tomato juice pH 4.0 and lemon juice pH 2.0. Care must be taken, however, not to allow high levels of food poisoning bacteria to get into low-acid foods (below pH 4) as they may survive for several days.

Atmosphere

Most bacteria require oxygen to multiply, but some can multiply in low levels of oxygen or do not need oxygen at all:

- obligate aerobes need oxygen – for example, *Bacillus cereus*

- obligate anaerobes multiply without oxygen and tend to cause problems in canning – for example, *Clostridium botulinum*

- facultative anaerobes multiply with or without oxygen – for example, *Salmonella* species and *Staphylococcus aureus*

Destruction of bacteria

Bacteria may be killed by:

- chemicals – a wide range of additives, including salt, sugar, nitrates, nitrites and sulphur dioxide, is available to prevent bacterial spoilage

- heat – temperatures above 63°C can destroy bacteria

- irradiation – which is legal only for certain foods (such as herbs and spices).

Chapter 4
Bacterial food poisoning

Bacterial food poisoning is an acute disturbance of the gastro-intestinal tract resulting in abdominal pain, with or without diarrhoea or vomiting. The illness is caused by the consumption of food (or water) that has been contaminated by specific pathogenic bacteria or their toxins.

Common food poisoning bacteria

Three pathogenic bacteria are responsible for most cases of bacterial food poisoning in the UK – *Salmonella* species, *Clostridium perfringens* and *Staphylococcus aureus*. (It is important to note that *Campylobacter jejuni*, which is the most common cause of diarrhoea, causes a food-borne disease, not food poisoning – *see* Chapter 5.)

	% of reported cases
Salmonella	80 %
Clostridium perfringens	5 to 15 %
Staphylococcus aureus	1 to 4 %

Food poisoning symptoms caused by *Salmonella* are generally severe and this largely explains why it is responsible for the majority of reported cases of food poisoning.

Bacillus cereus

Escherichia coli

Clostridium botulinum

Salmonella enteritidis

Clostridium perfringens

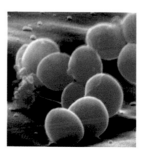

Staphylococcus aureus

Characteristics of the main food poisoning bacteria

Bacillus cereus
This is an aerobic spore-forming bacterium that produces a heat resistant exotoxin.

Source	Cereals, soil, dust, vegetation and spices.
Food commonly involved	Rice and rice dishes. Also found in soy sauce and products containing cornflour.
Cause of illness	A heat-resistant exotoxin produced by the bacteria as they multiply in food.
Illness	Onset time: 1–5 hours after eating contaminated food. Symptoms include nausea, vomiting, abdominal pain and some diarrhoea. Duration: 12–24 hours. Occasionally the exotoxin acts as an endotoxin causing illness 12–16 hours after eating contaminated food. In these circumstances, the main symptom is diarrhoea.
Carrier status	None.
Control measures	Thorough cooking and rapid cooling of food. Storage under refrigeration. Avoidance of reheating. Preventing cross-contamination.

Clostridium botulinum
This anaerobic spore-forming bacterium rarely causes food poisoning in Britain. The illness is life-threatening in 5–10% of cases. *Clostridium botulinum* produces a heat-sensitive neurotoxin.

Source	Soil, meat and fish – in certain parts of the world. The spores can survive cooking and other processes such as canning.
Food commonly involved	Canned salmon, smoked fish, vacuum-packed meat, bottled vegetables and herbs in oil.
Cause of illness	A heat-sensitive neurotoxin produced by the bacteria as it multiplies in food.
Illness	Onset time: 12–36 hours after eating contaminated food. Symptoms include fatigue, headache and diarrhoea at first, followed by damage to the nervous system and disturbed vision and speech. Death occurs within eight days of the onset of symptoms unless an anti-toxin is given.
Carrier status	None.
Control measures	High standards achieved in the preservation of food, especially canning (for 'botulinum cook' *see* page 56), bottling and vacuum packing. Avoiding eating raw and fermented fish in certain areas of the world. Inspecting cans and their contents before use and discarding 'blown' or damaged cans or unsatisfactory contents.

Characteristics of the main food poisoning bacteria (continued)

Clostridium perfringens

This rod-shaped anaerobic bacterium forms spores and an endotoxin.

Source	Human and animal intestines, soil, dust, flies, raw meat and poultry. Some dried products can be contaminated.
Food commonly involved	Meat and vegetables such as potatoes and carrots.
Cause of illness	An endotoxin. Bacteria multiply rapidly in meat that is cooked slowly or in cooked meat that is stored at an ambient temperature. Spores form in adverse conditions such as high temperatures. Once conditions are more favourable, the spores regenerate into bacteria. Toxins are released when the bacteria die in the host's intestines. The infective dose is 1,000,000 per gram of food.
Illness	Onset time: 8–22 (usually 12–18) hours after eating contaminated food.
	Symptoms include abdominal pain and diarrhoea. Vomiting is unusual. The illness can be fatal to those who are at an increased risk, such as the elderly.
	Duration: 1–2 days.
Carrier status	Possible.
Control measures	Strict temperature control:
	– cut meat into small joints or portions before cooking
	– cool hot food rapidly.
	Separation of raw and cooked foods.
	Regular removal of all dirt from food areas.
	Careful washing of vegetables.

Escherichia coli

Most types of this group of aerobic rod-shaped bacteria are harmless, but a few strains can cause food poisoning and are responsible for 'travellers' diarrhoea' and severe diarrhoea in very young babies and children.

A particular strain of the bacterium, known as *E. coli* O157, produces an extremely virulent toxin referred to as a verocytotoxin. This is responsible for many cases of food-borne disease – see page 29.

Source	Human and animal intestines, raw meat and sewage. The bacteria are an indicator of poor personal hygiene standards and the contamination of water by sewage.
Food commonly involved	Raw meat, undercooked beefburgers, gravy, raw milk.
Cause of illness	An enterotoxin.
Illness	Onset time: 12–24 hours after eating contaminated food.
	Symptoms usually include abdominal pain, fever, diarrhoea and vomiting. The illness is not serious for most healthy individuals but it can be fatal especially to vulnerable groups such as the young, old, ill and convalescing.
	Duration: 1–5 days.
Carrier status	The bacteria are naturally present in the human intestine.
Control measures	Separation of raw and high-risk foods and different work areas to prevent cross-contamination.
	Thorough cooking and temperature control of chilled ready-to-eat foods
	Good personal hygiene to prevent cross-contamination.
	Safe sources of drinking water and safe disposal of sewage.

Characteristics of the main food poisoning bacteria (continued)

Salmonella

Salmonella species cause the majority and most serious cases of bacterial food poisoning in the UK. There are approximately 2,400 serotypes, of which the most common are *Salmonella enteritidis* and *Salmonella typhimurium*. The bacteria are facultative anaerobic bacilli (rod-shaped bacteria).

Source	Human and animal intestines and excreted stools. The route into food areas is in raw foods of animal origin – meat, poultry, sausages, milk, eggs and egg products – or in animal excreta and fertilisers – for instance, on vegetables.
	Food pests and domestic pets are also sources.
Food commonly involved	Meat, poultry, eggs, milk.
Cause of illness	Large numbers of the bacteria living in the food. The bacteria need to multiply extensively before they can cause illness – the infective dose is usually in excess of 100,000 organisms per gram of food.
Illness	Onset time: 12–72 hours, usually 12–36 hours, after eating contaminated food.
	Symptoms include fever, headache, abdominal pain, diarrhoea (often watery and sometimes bloody) and vomiting. The illness can be fatal especially to vulnerable groups such as the young, old, ill and convalescing.
	Duration: 1–7 days.
Carrier status	May be carried in the human intestine.
Control measures	Separation of raw and high-risk foods and work areas.
	Thorough cleaning and disinfection.
	Thorough thawing and cooking of poultry and meat.
	Good personal hygiene.
	Effective pest control.

Staphylococcus aureus

This sphere-shaped bacterium is a facultative anaerobe that tolerates salt and produces an exotoxin.

Source	People – from the skin, nose, hands, throat and hair. Also found in boils, carbuncles, whitlows, styes, septic lesions, burns and scratches.
	Raw milk from cows and goats – the organism and its toxin can also be found in cream and cheese.
Food commonly involved	Milk, cream, cooked meats.
Cause of illness	A heat-resistant exotoxin produced by the bacteria as they multiply on food.
Illness	Onset time: 1–7 (usually 2–4) hours after eating contaminated food.
	Symptoms include acute vomiting, abdominal pain, diarrhoea and sometimes collapse.
	Duration: not more than 24 hours.
Carrier status	Common.
Control measures	Good personal hygiene.
	Temperature and time control when cooking, cooling and reheating.
	Effective food hygiene.

The role of the supervisor

Steps to take if food poisoning occurs:

- Notify the food business operator – who may inform the environmental health practitioner (EHP) – when a case of food poisoning occurs or is suspected.

- Tell any employee with food poisoning or suspected food poisoning to stay off work until he or she has seen a doctor and been cleared as safe to return to work with food.

- Leave the area uncleaned until the EHP or the food business operator is satisfied that it can be cleaned without interfering with the investigation.

- Remove from sale any food suspected of causing illness and, where appropriate, recall any suspect food that has been sold.

- Keep samples of suspected food and any unused food.

- Provide records and information – on issues such as personnel, sickness, food purchases, traceability and temperature control – for the officer carrying out an investigation into any food-borne illness.

- Assist the investigating EHP – for example, by providing a room or other facilities.

- Assist in the review of food safety management procedures.

- Follow any recommendations to prevent a recurrence of the problem.

Chapter 5
Food-borne disease

Food-borne diseases are often associated with contaminated water sources as well as with contaminated food and are responsible for many outbreaks of serious illness. In food-borne diseases, the food acts as a vehicle for the pathogen that does not have to multiply in the food before causing illness. Instead, the pathogen multiplies in the person who has eaten the food.

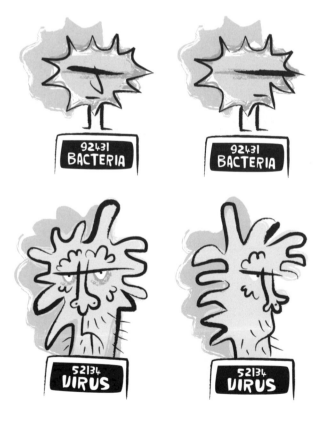

Campylobacter enteritis

Campylobacter enteritis (causative organisms *Campylobacter jejuni* and *Campylobacter coli*) is currently the most common cause of diarrhoea and is responsible for over 40,000 laboratory reports of faecal isolates per year in England and Wales. Often associated with animals, untreated water, raw meat and poultry (undercooked poultry, in particular) the source of most infections is still unknown.

E. coli O157

E. coli O157 and, in particular, verocytotoxin producing (VTEC) type causes a severe disease that can be fatal particularly for vulnerable groups (infants, young children and elderly people). Following a large outbreak in Scotland in 1996 involving cooked meat and gravy from a butcher's shop, there were over 500 cases and 18 elderly people died. This outbreak still remains the largest outbreak caused by this organism in the UK. Between 1995 and 2000 106 general outbreaks were reported. An outbreak in South Wales in 2005 involved over 150 school-age children in more than 40 schools. One child, aged five, died. The outbreak was possibly linked to a cooked meat supplier to a centralised school meals unit. The main source in the UK for *E. coli* O157 (VTEC) is the intestines of healthy cattle – meat carcasses can become contaminated at slaughter if hygiene standards are poor. This has brought about tighter regulation of abattoir practices in recent years. The organism is of particular concern as the infective dose may be as low as 10–100 organisms and the symptoms can be particularly severe in young children, causing kidney damage and failure.

Listeriosis

Listeriosis (causative organism *Listeria monocytogenes*) is present in the environment – in soil, water, vegetation, human and animal faeces – and can be found in a wide range of foods. It is not highly pathogenic to most healthy adults. However, pregnant women, elderly and immuno-compromised persons (for example, people who are HIV positive or recovering from a major operation) are particularly at risk. In pregnant women, the illness can cause premature birth or stillbirth or the baby may develop meningitis after birth. Unlike most pathogenic bacteria, *Listeria monocytogenes* can multiply slowly at refrigeration temperatures. Products, such as meat-based pates and soft cheese, that may be refrigerated for extended periods could be potentially hazardous if consumed by at-risk groups. Such individuals are, therefore, advised to avoid these products.

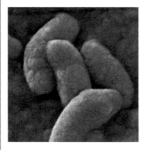

Campylobacter enteritis – the most common cause of diarrhoea

Cooked meat and gravy have been linked to *E. coli* O157

Food poisoning and food-borne disease

There are several basic differences between these two types of food-borne illness:

- The incubation period (or onset time) for food-borne diseases is often much longer than for food poisoning and is typically 1–11 days. The incubation period for Listeriosis may be as long as 70 days. This contrasts with the food poisoning onset times for *Bacillus cereus* (1–5 hours) and *Staphylococcus aureus* (1–7 hours).

- The infective dose for food-borne diseases is smaller than that for food poisoning. For example, only 500 *Campylobacter jejuni* can cause illness and in the case of verocytotoxin (VTEC) *E. coli* O157 the infective dose may be less than 100 organisms. The infective doses for food poisoning organisms are generally much higher – approximately 100,000 organisms per gram of food for *Salmonella* or 1,000,000 organisms per gram of food for *Clostridium perfringens*.

- In contrast to food poisoning bacteria, the multiplication of pathogenic organisms in food is not an essential feature of food-borne disease as the food merely acts as a vehicle for the pathogen.

- Food-borne diseases may be spread by items other than food. Food poisoning bacteria in contrast need food in order to multiply to sufficient levels to cause illness, either by the bacteria themselves and/or their toxins.

- The infective organism of food-borne diseases may enter the blood stream.

- The symptoms of food-borne diseases may or may not include diarrhoea and vomiting.

Food-borne disease may be spread by means other than food

Viruses

Viruses have been included in this section as, in common with bacteria causing food-borne disease, they do not have to multiply in the food before causing illness and use food purely as a vehicle to enter the body. They are much smaller than bacteria – by up to a hundred times – and are measured in nanometers (nm) or billionths of a meter.

Unlike food poisoning bacteria, which need certain types of food to thrive, viruses do not depend upon any kind of food for their survival. This means that all food is susceptible to contamination by viruses. It is only after a virus has been eaten that it can multiply, and it does so in human tissue. The infective dose is generally very low.

Norovirus

Norovirus (originally called the Norwalk-like virus or small, round-structured virus, SRSV) is the most common cause of gastro-enteritis in England and Wales. The Health Protection Agency estimates that it affects approximately one million people in the UK each year. Sources include sewage-contaminated water, water-filtering shellfish (such as oysters and mussels), raw vegetables and salad and it is commonly spread person to person by the faecal-oral route. The incubation period is 1–2 days and the symptoms, which include nausea, vomiting (often projectile), diarrhoea, abdominal pain and fever, typically last for 1–3 days. The illness is common and spreads very quickly where people are in confined environments, such as hospitals, care and nursing homes and schools. It always causes wide publicity when it occurs on a cruise ship – another ideal environment for it to spread quickly. Norovirus is also called the 'winter vomiting disease' as there is usually a peak of activity in winter.

Hepatitis A

Hepatitis A is a viral infection spread mainly by the faecal-oral route, sewage-contaminated water, water-filtering shellfish (such as oysters and mussels), raw vegetables or any food that has been contaminated by handling. The incubation period averages 28 days and the illness, which initially causes fever, nausea, abdominal pain and a mild gastrointestinal upset, can progress to jaundice and can last from a week to several months.

Outbreaks of viral infection (such as Hepatitis A), as well as enteric fever (typhoid and paratyphoid) have been caused by eating shellfish gathered from sewage-polluted water that has not been correctly prepared before consumption. Treatment systems are used in Britain to purify oysters and mussels. Where these procedures are generally effective with bacteria, however, this is not always the case with viruses.

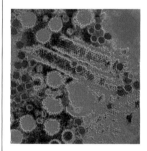

Norovirus

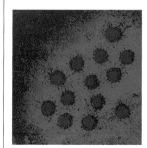

Hepatitis A

Food-borne diseases

Disease	Causative organism(s)	Sources	Incubation period
Campylobacter enteritis	*Campylobacter jejuni* (90 % of cases) and *Campylobacter coli* (10 % of cases)	Animals (including wild animals), untreated water, raw meat, offal, poultry and untreated milk.	1–11 days Normally 2–5 days
E. coli (NB also a food poisoning organism – see page 25)	*Escherichia coli.* Some types, such as *E. coli 0157*, produce a verocytotoxin (VTEC)	Raw meat (especially minced meats – beefburgers), raw milk, water, salads and fruits. Spread maybe by food, water, sewage, or person to person.	1–6 days
Listeriosis	*Listeria monocytogenes*	Widely distributed in the environment. Soil, water, vegetation, human and animal faeces. Foods include cook/chill products, pates, soft cheeses, prepared salads, dairy products and salami.	3–70 days
Typhoid and paratyphoid	*Salmonella typhi* (typhoid) and *Salmonella paratyphi* (paratyphoid)	Faeces of infected people, contaminated water, shellfish, raw milk, raw fruit, vegetables and salads	7–21 days for both typhoid and paratyphoid
Bacillary dysentery	*Shigella sonnei* and *Shigella flexneri*	Faeces of infected people, contaminated water, shellfish, milk, raw vegetables and salads	1–7 days. 4 days is common
Viral gastroenteritis	*Norovirus*	Sewage-contaminated water, water-filtering shellfish, raw vegetables and salad. Person to person (faecal-oral route)	1–2 days
Hepatitis A	*Hepatovirus*	Sewage-contaminated water, water-filtering shellfish, raw vegetables and salad. Person to person (faecal-oral route) Any food that has contaminated by handling	10–50 days

Symptoms	Carrier status	Control measures
Abdominal pain, diarrhoea, fever and headache. Flu-like symptoms	Long-term carriers have been detected	Thorough hand washing, especially after handling raw meats Preventing cross contamination Thorough cooking Avoid contact with animals/pets Chlorination of water supplies Pasteurisation of milk
Acute abdominal pain, bloody diarrhoea, kidney damage and kidney failure. Life threatening.	Yes	Strict control of slaughter procedures and hygiene Separation of raw and cooked foods Thorough cooking, especially minced meat products Good personal hygiene Careful, thorough washing of salads and fruit. Pasteurisation
Fever, septicaemia, meningitis, abortion	Yes	Avoidance of high-risk foods – in particular soft cheese and pate – by pregnant women Avoidance of cross-contamination at all stages from 'farm to fork' Thorough cooking /reheating (e.g. cook/chill products) Washing of vegetables and salads to be eaten raw Strict stock control of 'at-risk' products
Typhoid – progressive fever, headache, profuse diarrhoea, 'rose spots' Paratyphoid – as typhoid, but milder	Yes	Use of satisfactory water supply – not contaminated by sewage Proper sewage disposal Exclusion of infected food handlers Good personal hygiene Thorough cleaning and disinfection Effective pest control (flies and rodents in particular) Use of approved suppliers Heat treatment of milk
Diarrhoea (may be bloody), fever, stomach cramps and vomiting	Yes	Use of satisfactory water supply – not contaminated by sewage Proper sewage disposal Exclusion of infected food handlers Good personal hygiene Thorough cleaning and disinfection Effective pest control (flies and rodents in particular) Use of approved suppliers Heat treatment of milk
Nausea, vomiting (often projectile), diarrhoea, abdominal pain, fever	Yes	Safe water supply – not contaminated with sewage (especially irrigation water) Approved suppliers Washing of raw vegetables and salad Exclusion of infected food handlers Good personal hygiene
Fever, nausea, abdominal pain, jaundice (may last for several months)	Yes	Safe water supply – not contaminated with sewage (especially irrigation water) Approved suppliers Washing of raw vegetables and salad Exclusion of infected food handlers Good personal hygiene

Chapter 6
Non-bacterial food poisoning

Bacteria are the main cause of food poisoning but illness can also be caused by chemicals, metals, poisonous plants, poisonous fish and mycotoxins.

Chemical food poisoning

Chemical food poisoning is rare but, when it does occur, the consequences can be very serious. The symptoms may be acute or chronic. Acute symptoms, which have an onset of less than one hour, include vomiting, diarrhoea and burning sensations in the mouth, neck, chest, and abdomen. With chronic poisoning, the chemical builds up in the body over a period of time, causing a variety of problems such as joint pain, cancer and damage to the nervous system.

The causes of chemical food poisoning, which may be due to negligence or deliberate fraud, include:

- excessive quantities of pesticide sprayed onto fruit and vegetables as they grow
- misuse of antibiotics during the rearing of animals
- environmental contamination of soil or water
- misuse of cleaning chemicals at food premises
- incorrect storage of cleaning materials, weedkiller or pesticides – for example, storage of chemicals near food or storage of chemicals in unlabelled food containers
- the use of chemical food additives in excess of permitted levels
- fraud – for example, olive oil sold in Spain was contaminated by a toxic substance and Austrian wine was contaminated by anti-freeze type chemicals
- deliberate tampering.

Food poisoning from metals

Metals can enter the human food chain from the soil if they are absorbed by animals as they graze or by vegetables, fruit and cereals as they grow. Fish caught in polluted waters may be contaminated by metals. Problems may also occur if food, especially very acidic food, comes into contact with metals such as:

- antimony – typically from the enamel coating of cooking equipment
- cadmium – from cookers, refrigerator shelves and some types of earthenware pots and dishes
- copper – usually from cooking utensils and some instances where copper pipes have contaminated cold soft drinks or milk dispensed by machines
- lead – from some types of earthenware, lead crystal or ceramics
- tin and iron – usually from cans
- zinc – typically from galvanised equipment.

Food poisoning can be caused if metals – such as antimony or copper – come into contact with acidic food

Poisonous plants

The main causes of such poisoning in Britain are:

- poisonous plants and fungi eaten accidentally – such as poisonous mushrooms, rhubarb leaves and plants including deadly nightshade and more common members of the nightshade family, such as bittersweet
- incorrectly processed beans, such as red kidney beans and haricot beans
- incorrectly stored potatoes that have turned green: potatoes belong to the same botanical family – *Solanum* – as the poisonous nightshade plants noted above.

Red kidney beans must be cooked at a high enough temperature to destroy the naturally occurring toxin haemagglutinin that causes poisoning. Typical symptoms usually occurring within a few hours of eating undercooked beans are nausea, vomiting and abdominal pain. The use of slow cookers, which may only reach around 70°C, is not sufficient. Beans that have been soaked in cold water for several hours need to be rinsed and then placed in vigorously boiling water for 15 minutes. The use of canned kidney beans, which have already been processed, is recommended.

Potatoes that have been stored in the light, and in particular when they start to sprout and turn green, produce a toxic chemical, solanine, which can cause nausea, dizziness and burning sensations in the mouth. Potatoes cooked in their skins are most hazardous as the toxin is not destroyed.

Green potatoes produce a toxic chemical – solanine

Poisonous fish

Scombrotoxic fish poisoning

This illness is caused by toxins produced in some dark-fleshed fish, such as mackerel, tuna and sardines, during storage. Refrigerating the fish as soon as it is caught reduces the problem, but once spoilage has occurred, the toxin cannot be destroyed whether the fish is smoked, soused or canned. The typical average onset period is ten minutes to three hours. The symptoms, which last up to eight hours, include headache, nausea, vomiting, abdominal pain, diarrhoea, rashes and a burning sensation in the mouth.

Ciguatera poisoning

This life-threatening illness arises from eating reef-dwelling fish, such as barracudas, sea basses, groupers and eels, which have fed on types of marine algae (or other algae-eating marine creatures) that produce a toxin. The fish are unaffected by the toxin but about 300 varieties of fish caught in the Pacific and Caribbean can poison humans. The symptoms include sickness, diarrhoea and throat and respiratory problems, and may be fatal. The onset time is one to six hours.

Paralytic shellfish poisoning and diarrhetic shellfish poisoning

The sources of these potentially fatal illnesses are mussels and other bivalve molluscs that have fed on plankton that produce neurotoxins. The toxins can survive cooking. Symptoms of paralytic shellfish poisoning appear immediately and progress within four to 12 hours from numbness of the mouth, then neck, arms and legs, to respiratory paralysis, which can lead to death. Diarrhetic shellfish poisoning may occur in a similar manner, but symptoms include diarrhoea and vomiting that last only a few days.

Dark-fleshed fish, reef-dwelling fish and bivalve molluscs can cause food poisoning

Mycotoxins

These poisons are produced by certain types of mould, such as some *Aspergillus* and *Penicillin* species, as they grow on food. They may cause vomiting and diarrhoea or may be carcinogenic (cancer causing). Foods that have been contaminated by mycotoxins include cereals, nuts, apple juice, herbs, spices, milk and milk powder.

Moulds that produce mycotoxins can multiply in conditions where generally bacteria are unable to survive – for example, low pH, low a_w and temperatures below 0°C. In the case of cereals their formation can be prevented by rapid drying after harvest followed by storage in dry conditions. They can carry over into milk and meat when cows are given feed that contains mycotoxins. This situation is complicated further by the fact that mycotoxins can survive pasteurisation processes and even sterilisation. Therefore, careful control at all stages in the food chain is vital in preventing the formation of mycotoxins.

Chapter 7
Food spoilage

Food starts to decompose as soon as it is harvested or slaughtered, so storage methods and conditions should aim to reduce the rate of decomposition to safeguard the nutritional value, appearance, taste and fitness of the food.

Changes to food

Once plant or animal tissue has died, there is no longer any protection from the attack of bacteria, moulds and yeasts, or from the activity of enzymes that may be present either in the plant or animal tissue itself or in micro-organisms on the food. The rate of decomposition depends on the type of food and/or the way in which it is handled. Food may be considered spoiled when it is undesirable or unfit to eat. When food may be considered spoiled depends, to some extent, upon individual taste – for example, some people like mature cheese, very ripe fruit or game that has been hung for some time.

Not all the changes that take place in food after harvesting or slaughtering are undesirable. For example, the conversion of sugars to alcohol enables wine and beer to be made, while the souring of milk is essential in the production of cheese. Some enzymes are deliberately used in the food industry to produce specific effects, such as to tenderise meat. However, most changes impair the acceptability of food and some may be harmful to health.

Common indications of spoilage include changes to the food that affect its:

- appearance – for example, discoloration or slime
- smell
- texture
- taste.

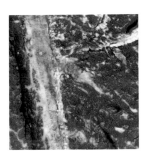

Spoilage can cause changes to the appearance, smell, texture and taste of food

The causes of food spoilage

Spoilage of food may be caused by:

- decomposition – due to enzymes and micro-organisms including bacteria, moulds and yeasts
- pest infestation – for example, by stored product insects (such as grain weevils and flour moths) or bluebottles feeding and/or laying eggs on meat
- physical damage, including freezer burn and oxidation – for example, where foods are inadequately packaged and stored for excessively long periods
- chemical contamination – for example, where foods are tainted by strong-smelling cleaning chemicals or perfumed soaps.

Most food spoilage is caused by mould. A network of fine strands, called a mycelium, which is formed by mould, is often visible on foods particularly when they have been stored in damp conditions.

The activities of natural enzymes continue after harvesting or slaughtering unless the enzymes are inactivated. Like bacteria, enzymes are inhibited by high and low temperatures although many remain active at temperatures as low as -2°C. For this reason vegetables are commercially blanched (usually by immersion in boiling water, or exposure to steam, for a short period) before freezing to destroy enzymes.

Some bacteria may be categorised as both pathogenic and spoilage. For example, the food poisoning bacteria *Clostridium perfringens* and *Bacillus cereus* are also common causes of spoilage in meat and poultry (*Clostridium perfringens*) and milk and cream (*Bacillus cereus*).

The storage of foods

While food is stored, it should be protected from taint and contamination. Microbes and enzymes can be inhibited by high and low temperatures. There is more specific information on both storage and temperature control in Chapter 10 'Storage and temperature control'.

Legal considerations

It is illegal to have unfit food that is intended for human consumption on food premises. Unfit food in food premises is presumed to be for human consumption unless it is clearly identified and segregated. Environmental health practitioners may seize unfit food and ask a magistrate or sheriff to condemn it. Once condemned, it must be destroyed.

Most food spoilage is caused by mould

Unfit food should be clearly identified and segregated

Part 2: Controls

Chapter 8
Control of contamination

There will always be food safety hazards but they can be controlled if you understand how food becomes contaminated and, more importantly, how to prevent it from happening.

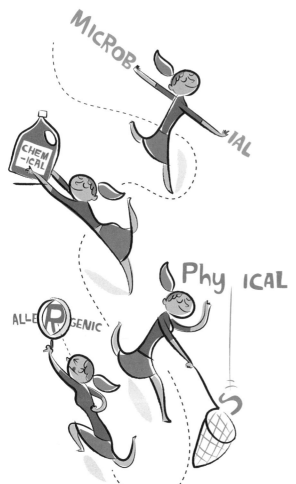

How contamination occurs

Contamination can occur at any stage 'from farm to fork':

- a stone can be missed when vegetables are visually checked on a conveyor belt prior to packing
- carcasses of meat may be stored on the floor of a delivery vehicle and pick up dirt
- a waterproof dressing can accidentally come off while handling food and end up in a finished product
- a disinfectant not properly rinsed off a work surface may taint food.

With physical and chemical contamination it is often quite easy to identify how it occurred. This is generally not the case with microbial contamination.

Microbial contamination may occur when:

- raw food touches high-risk food or when liquid from a raw food drips onto a high-risk food (direct contamination)
- bacteria are transferred from a raw food to a high-risk food by, for example, hands (cross-contamination).

Cross-contamination involves 'vehicles of contamination' that enable bacteria to move from one surface to another. Vehicles of contamination include:

- hands
- equipment – knives, chopping boards, mixing bowls
- cloths
- food- or hand-contact surfaces.

Sources
Humans, raw foods, insects, animals, rodents, the environment, dust and soil

Mobile vehicles of contamination
Hands, equipment, clothes

High-risk foods

Stationary vehicles of contamination
Food- or hand-contact surfaces

Preventing bacterial contamination

There are some simple principles for preventing bacterial contamination:

1. Protect food from contamination:
   - separate raw and high-risk food to avoid cross-contamination
   - ensure that food is covered
   - maintain high standards of personal hygiene
   - ensure that the premises are clean.

2. Prevent bacterial multiplication:
   - keep high-risk food out of danger zone temperatures (5°C to 63°C) as much as possible
   - remember that cooked food may contain bacterial spores: if it is kept at a temperature in the danger zone, the spores may germinate and bacteria may then multiply
   - use and maintain suitable and efficient cold storage facilities
   - ensure that hot foods are cooled rapidly.

3. Destroy bacteria:
   - cook to destroy bacteria (but remember that spores may survive)
   - serve food immediately after cooking
   - if cooked food cannot be served at once, keep it hot at 63°C or above.

4. Remove contaminated food from the human food chain:
   - recall and rework or destroy it
   - dispose of it safely.

Preventing viral contamination

Encourage food handlers and others in the workplace to maintain high standards of personal hygiene, including washing their hands regularly with care. Ensure that staff understand the importance of, and follow, the workplace procedures for reporting sickness and other illnesses that could lead to the contamination of food (*see page 81*). Buy raw materials and food from reputable suppliers.

Preventing mould growth

Keep food covered and throw away any that has become mouldy. Packaged food, such as vacuum packed or canned items, should be handled and unpacked with care to prevent tearing or piercing the packaging, which would allow mould spores to settle on the food.

Protect food from contamination

Preventing physical contamination

General measures to prevent physical contamination will vary depending on the type of operation, but may include:

- inspection of raw materials on receipt
- cleaning, washing and inspecting raw materials before use
- filtering liquids and sieving powders – this may be a manual operation or involve in-line filters or sieves, such as in a brewery or a flour mill
- protecting filling hoppers, elevators and belts conveying open food from overhead contamination
- selecting machinery with guards that are easy to remove and clean
- avoiding temporary repairs – for example, using string or tape instead of correct spare parts
- employing spotters at inspection belts – for example, removing stalks, leaves and other extraneous matter when preparing fruit and vegetables for packing
- visual checking of food before it leaves the production area
- in-line magnets to collect metal fragments in pipe-work for bulk movement of liquids and solids
- metal detectors (for ferrous and non-ferrous metals) – usually located at end of a continuous production line, just after food has been packed prior to despatch to final point of sale
- X-ray machines – again usually located on large throughput production lines and used for the detection and rejection of non-magnetic items such as glass, plastic, wood, insects
- bottle scanners – beams of light travel through the container onto a photo-electric cell, if a beam of light is broken – for example, by a speck of dirt – the bottle is automatically rejected.

Prevent physical contamination by checking food at all stages of production

People

People are a common source of physical contaminants, such as:

- hair
- fingernails
- sweet papers
- cigarettes
- jewellery.

Staff should not eat sweets, chew gum or smoke in food areas – food businesses have a responsibility to explain the hazards to food handlers and supervise them carefully. Company policy should ensure that food handlers do not wear jewellery and that all staff maintain high standards of personal hygiene. Suitable protective clothing, including hair covering, must be worn correctly. Pens and other writing implements should not be used where they could contaminate food – for instance, near open hoppers and mixing tanks.

Food may be contaminated by food handlers, other members of staff who do not normally handle food (such as maintenance engineers), visitors (including engineers, painters and sales representatives) and customers.

Contamination by customers may be accidental or deliberate. The food industry has invested in tamper-proof seals and other devices designed to prevent the deliberate contamination of products for sabotage or blackmail. Staff may also deliberately contaminate food for malicious, mischievous or financial reasons and many food businesses have a policy of not allowing dismissed staff to continue to work through their leave period.

Suitable protective clothing, including hair covering, must be worn correctly

Packing materials

Cardboard, polythene, string, plastic, wood, metal, staples and other similar items may get into food from packaging around raw materials or a finished product. Food should, therefore, be unpacked in a separate area where there is no open food. All unwanted packaging must be placed in lidded containers and removed as soon as possible. It should be specified that suppliers' cardboard cartons be glued and/or taped rather than stapled.

Pests

Fur, feathers, droppings, eggs, larvae and dead bodies of pests can all cause contamination. Some pest contaminants are taken into food premises in raw foods and ingredients, but food can also be contaminated on the premises if there is an infestation. Contaminated food must be rejected and appropriate control measures used to treat the infestation. Pest control contractors should inspect food premises on a regular basis and be on call for the immediate treatment of infestations. Preventive measures, such as fly screens at doors and windows, are useful controls (*see* Chapter 14).

Design and structure

Machinery and structural items can cause physical contamination – such as glass from windows or light bulbs, flakes of paint from walls or pipes, fragments of plaster from walls and rust from machines or pipes. Premises should be maintained in good condition and staff should be encouraged to report defects.

Grease and oil may be considered either physical or chemical contaminants. Food-grade lubricants should always be used in food machinery and motors should not be positioned above open food. If necessary, non-corroding, easy-to-clean drip trays should be fixed under motors to catch any drips.

Bolts, nuts and screws should be non-corroding and positioned so that they cannot contaminate food if they become loose and fall. Ideally, nuts should be self-locking.

Maintenance and repairs

Engineers, maintenance staff and contractors must be instructed not to leave loose fittings in food rooms. Supervisors should check the work area after repair and maintenance work has finished and before food production restarts. Special precautions and procedures should be taken if maintenance or repair work has to be carried out in food production or storage areas. Such steps include:

- covering or removing all food
- checking that all equipment brought in is removed when work is completed – it should be signed in and out
- cleaning the area before work with food restarts
- checking that machines are re-assembled correctly.

After maintenance work, clean thoroughly before work with food restarts

Wood

Wherever possible wooden containers for raw materials should be avoided to prevent wood splinters from contaminating food. For the same reason wooden pallets are not usually permitted in food premises apart from immediate in-coming goods storage areas or areas where finished packaged goods are boxed or prepared for palletised distribution. Hard plastic pallets should be used in all other food preparation areas.

Wood should not be used for food preparation surfaces, either tables or chopping boards. In addition to the risk of physical contamination from splinters, wood is also a microbiological hazard as it is likely to be porous and, therefore, absorb and hold bacteria. Wooden preparation tables should be replaced with stainless steel and chopping boards with hard plastic. Hard plastic chopping boards also have the added advantage of being available in many colours allowing colour-coding of equipment to be introduced.

Any manual cleaning equipment with wooden handles and/or natural bristles should be replaced with all-plastic food grade versions.

Glass

Unless used to contain the final product, the use of glass should be avoided in food rooms. Plastic or wired glass should be used for windows and diffusers should be fitted to all fluorescent tubes to prevent glass from scattering if a tube is broken.

Should glass be broken in a food preparation area:

- a staff member should notify the supervisor
- the supervisor should stop the production line and other work where contamination is likely
- all glass should be removed, possibly by using a vacuum cleaner
- all products and open ingredients near the breakage area should be examined and, if necessary, discarded.

In automated processes, other containers near the broken one may also be rejected automatically.

Where glass is used for the final product container:

- bottles/jars should be washed and inverted until they are filled
- mechanical and human spotters should be used to check for contamination
- a policy on glass breakage should be formulated and implemented
- all glass covers, windows and other fixtures and implements should be regularly checked as part of a glass audit.

Glass containers must be checked for contamination and faults

Containers

Single-use containers

Single-use containers are generally preferred to returnable ones, which may be contaminated by customers. Single-use containers should be cleaned immediately before use, inverted, then inspected before filling is carried out. Depending on the size and/or speed of the operation this may be a visual inspection with spotters or automatic, using detection equipment. Any bottle breakages should be reported and the production line stopped. All broken glass must be cleared up and any bottles that could have become contaminated should be checked before production resumes.

Returnable bottles

Very dirty or cracked bottles should be removed before bottles go to be washed. Bottle washing machines should be well maintained, operated at the correct temperature and dosed with the correct quantity of detergent and disinfectant in accordance with the manufacturer's instructions.

Staff should watch out for and remove any dirty or damaged bottles as they come out of the washer. The spotters should be allowed to rotate tasks to help them to maintain their concentration. Black and white backgrounds for empty bottles and mirrors behind filled bottles help staff to detect faulty containers. If scanners are used to detect dirt, there should be regular checks to ensure that the scanners are working correctly.

Preventing chemical contamination

Raw materials

Regulations limit the amount of chemicals, such as pesticides and preservatives, which may be used on or in food. Some manufacturers test for pesticides before using raw materials or request certificates of analysis from suppliers. Suppliers may also be subjected to routine audit.

If additives are used, procedures must be in place to check that they are used safely.

Cleaning materials

Chemicals used for cleaning purposes must be unperfumed and safe for use in food areas. All chemicals must be kept in correctly labelled containers in a controlled storage area separated from food. Staff should receive specific training in the safe use of chemicals.

Food handlers

Staff should be trained to understand the problems caused by the use of highly scented soap, perfume, aftershave and other products. All soap provided by the food business should be unperfumed.

Metal pots, pans and food containers

Food businesses should ensure that all utensils and containers are suitable for the food that is in contact with them. Supervisors should ensure that staff use the correct items for each task.

Control of allergens

How allergens are controlled will vary depending on the particular food sector. However, in all situations it is vital that systems are in place to ensure that allergens do not contaminate food that is meant to be allergen free.

In the catering sector if a customer enquires whether or not a dish contains a specific ingredient, you must be able to identify all the ingredients that are used to make up that meal. This will include what is used to cook the dish – for example, is it fried in sunflower oil which may be acceptable, or ground nut oil which would not be acceptable for someone with a nut allergy – as well as what might be in any sauce, garnish or salad dressing. If it is a meal that is purchased ready-made, your supplier must provide information about all the ingredients used. People who suffer from severe allergic reactions can react to tiny quantities of allergens, so particular care must be taken when preparing allergen-free dishes. Include information about the allergens on menus – for example, pasta containing egg, carrot cake containing nuts, etc. (see pages 13 and 14 for more information on common allergens).

Staff need to be trained so that they understand the danger that certain foods can be to sensitive individuals and that, in addition to being aware of all the contents in a particular dish, they clean all surfaces and equipment before they start. They also need to know what to do in an emergency. If they think a customer is having a severe allergic reaction, and that it might be anaphylactic shock, they must seek immediate medical help by ringing the emergency services and requesting an ambulance.

In a retail outlet where open food is on display, further controls may be necessary. For example – segregated display of sensitive foods and separate utensils for serving can help to prevent cross-contamination. Clear labelling and ingredient information must be available for all products identifying the known presence of allergens or the potential risk of contamination at the point of manufacture. Again, staff training and awareness is vital.

Legislation requires that any pre-packed foods containing allergenic ingredients, or ingredients originating from allergenic ingredients, must be marked or labelled with a clear reference to the name of the allergenic ingredient (*see* opposite).

The allergy information for Haddock Cumberland Pie identifies that it contains cow's milk, fish, wheat, gluten and mustard. These can also all be identified from the ingredient list.

The allergy advice for the Roasted Red Pepper Humous is also quite specific in that it contains sesame seeds and sesame seed pulp make up 12 % of the product from the ingredient list.

In addition to identifying potential allergens in the ingredients list, the packaging for Organic Orange and Vanilla Flavoured Biscuits also states that it is 'not suitable for nut allergy sufferers' and that 'this product has been made in a factory that uses nut ingredients'.

The allergy advice for Pilau Rice indicates that it contains milk (i.e. from butter in the ingredient list). However, it also states that it is 'not suitable for nut or sesame allergy sufferers' neither of which are directly identifiable from the ingredient list. Either there were nut and sesame products on site when the product was manufactured, and/or a raw material supplier cannot guarantee that an ingredient they are supplying for use in the product is nut or sesame free.

The packaging examples on the previous page highlight the problems associated with allergens in a manufacturing situation. As only a tiny amount of an allergen may be required to initiate a severe allergic reaction – especially with nut allergy sufferers – it is often extremely difficult for a manufacturer to guarantee a product as totally allergen-free. Apart from the difficulty of cleaning a production line to remove all possible traces of an allergen, contamination can for example be carried as dust, on food handlers' protective clothing or via cleaning equipment. Therefore procedures need to be in place as part of a food safety management system to reduce the risk of allergen contamination on site and also to prevent contaminated product getting into the marketplace.

Procedures may include:

- auditing raw material suppliers
- only using reputable suppliers
- maintaining up-to-date allergen information on all raw materials on site
- clearly labelling packaging
- separate storage of raw materials that may contain allergens
- using separate processing equipment, utensils and production areas
- segregating staff in sensitive areas
- batch traceability for all raw materials and finished product
- separation and disposal procedures for contaminated raw materials and finished product
- specific allergy awareness training for staff
- product recall procedures.

To control the risk of allergen contamination provide allergen awareness training

Examples of supervisory management

The supervisory management role in preventing contamination will depend on the type and size of the food operation and the food safety hazards associated with the activity, but generally it is important to:

- purchase food and raw ingredients from known, reliable suppliers with high standards of hygiene, and test for quality
- accept deliveries only if they are transported in clean and properly equipped vehicles – refrigerated vehicles may be necessary
- inspect deliveries on arrival – reject any damaged, unfit or contaminated material, check the food temperature and date codes
- store deliveries in the correct place immediately
- keep any unfit food, chemicals and refuse away from stored foods
- keep high-risk foods apart from raw foods at all times
- consider the use of colour-coded knives, chopping boards and cleaning equipment (such as cloths and mops) to help staff to identify and use equipment for specific foods or food areas
- maintain good personal hygiene at all times and exclude potential carriers
- keep food covered unless it is being prepared – do not leave food unnecessarily in food areas
- keep premises, equipment and utensils clean and in good condition and repair – report any defects
- disinfect food-contact surfaces

- ensure that all empty containers are disinfected and clean before they are filled with food
- keep cleaning materials away from food and ensure that all cleaning residues, including dirty water, are rinsed from food equipment and pipes
- remove waste food and refuse from food areas as soon as practicable
- maintain an active pest control programme
- inspect food areas and processes frequently and act promptly to remedy any defects or unhygienic practices
- train staff thoroughly and monitor their work ensure that food is thawed adequately
- make suitable provisions for cooling food before refrigeration
- where possible, arrange for equipment to be removed from food areas for repair
- physically segregate areas under redecoration, alteration or maintenance from production areas
- control the access and movement of visitors and maintenance workers in high-risk areas
- ensure that maintenance workers wear clean clothing and do not stand on machinery or climb over open food
- designate separate areas, away from food, for decanting and unpacking.

Chapter 9
Food preservation

People have attempted to preserve food to prevent starvation from the earliest times. Foods with low moisture content, such as cereals, are easier to preserve than most moist, high protein foods, such as meat.

Potential hazards

- **Bacterial contamination** – if the preservation process is not carried out correctly or if a container, such as a can or a wrapper around vacuum-packed food, is damaged.

- **Cross-contamination** – if the preservation process is not controlled carefully.

- **Chemical contamination** – if an incorrect quantity of preservative, mould inhibitor or colouring is added or if containers are cleaned with excessive amounts of cleaning chemical or not rinsed thoroughly.

- **Physical contamination** – if containers are unclean or if raw ingredients are not cleaned and checked adequately before being processed.

Food preservation techniques

Food may be preserved in a variety of ways including the use of:

- low temperatures
- high temperatures
- dehydration
- chemical methods
- physical methods.

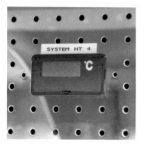

Refrigerators should operate at between 1°C and 4°C

Blast chillers are used to cool food rapidly

Low temperature preservation

This method of preservation relies upon the metabolic reactions of micro-organisms such as bacteria. In other words, the colder it is, the longer it takes for bacteria to multiply. They eventually become dormant and do not multiply at all (although they become active again if the temperature rises).

The temperatures involved are at:

- above freezing, for refrigeration
- freezing point (0°C), for commercial chilling (such as for chilled beef)
- below freezing (0°C and colder, typically -18°C to -23°C), for freezing.

Refrigeration

As best practice, refrigerators should operate at a temperature between 1°C and 4°C. They are suitable for storing most perishable foods for a short period. Most of the common pathogenic bacteria cease multiplication or producing toxins at temperatures below 5°C, although a few bacteria and moulds do multiply at low temperatures.

Commercial chilling

Raw meat may be held at temperatures between -1°C and 1°C for longer periods before sale than refrigerated meats.

Ideally, blast chillers are used to cool down hot foods quickly to around 5°C prior to refrigerated storage. Blast chillers, as the name suggests, are fan-assisted units that rapidly circulate chilled air around the product. The target is to achieve a temperature suitable for refrigeration as quickly as possible so that pathogens do not have an opportunity to multiply to unacceptable levels.

Freezing

Freezing relies on two processes to preserve food:

- the inhibition of enzyme activity
- the reduction of moisture (a_w) in the food.

The process of freezing destroys some pathogenic bacteria, but most merely become dormant. Many spores and toxins are unaffected by the freezing process. However, it is important to note that enzymes are very active at -2°C and can spoil food rapidly. Vegetables should be blanched (also *see* Chapter 7) before freezing to destroy enzymes and also to reduce the bacterial load.

Freezing may be fast or slow. Commercial freezers can freeze some food to -20°C in 30 minutes. However, a domestic-type appliance could take 72 hours. Rapid freezing is better because it prevents the formation of large ice crystals, which can affect the taste, texture and quality of the food after thawing, and reduces the loss of liquid during thawing.

Various methods of freezing exist including:

- **Air blast freezing** – fan-assisted freezing air is circulated over the food either in a freezer unit or a moving conveyor in a tunnel or spiral freezer. This is the most common method, used for ready meals, meat and fish products, confectionery products, pizza.
- **Fluidised bed freezing** – food is transported along a perforated belt on a cushion of freezing air allowing rapid freezing of individual items. Widely used for small vegetables such as peas.
- **Plate freezing** – blocks of food, for example fish fillets, inserted between metal plates and freezing air circulated around them.
- **Cryogenic freezing** – food is sprayed or immersed in liquid nitrogen for very quick freezing. An expensive method of freezing that is restricted to high-value products such as prawns, raspberries, strawberries.

Frozen food should be handled carefully to prevent contamination, particularly by *Staphylococcus aureus*.

Vegetables should be blanched before freezing

High temperature preservation

High temperatures are used to destroy both spoilage and pathogenic micro-organisms, thereby preserving the food. However, some heat-resistant bacteria, toxins and spores may survive. The number of micro-organisms that survive heat treatment depends on the:

- initial number of micro-organisms present
- type of organism
- duration of the heat treatment
- amount of protein and fat in the food
- pH of the food.

Precautions should be taken to prevent the recontamination of the food and to prevent conditions favourable to the multiplication of the remaining bacteria.

Cooking

Cooking helps to preserve food for a short time but its main purpose is to make the food more palatable and safe for immediate consumption. A core temperature of at least 70°C held for two minutes (or more commonly 75°C held for 30 seconds) is usually considered acceptable to ensure the destruction of pathogens.

Pasteurisation is the mildest form of heat treatment

Pasteurisation

Pasteurisation is the mildest form of heat treatment, allowing food to be made safe with minimal effect on flavour and nutritional value. Examples of its application include milk, eggs, large cans of ham, wine and canned fruit. The process destroys pathogens and large numbers of spoilage organisms, but spores, toxins and thermophilic spoilage bacteria usually survive. Therefore, pasteurised foods need to be refrigerated to prevent or slow down further spoilage.

Milk is usually pasteurised by heating to 72°C for 15 seconds then cooling rapidly to a refrigeration temperature. It is tested after pasteurisation for the enzyme phosphatase, which is found in raw milk. It should be absent.

Pasteurised liquid whole egg is widely used in manufacturing to avoid the hazards (from *Salmonella* species in particular) of handling large amounts of shell egg in food premises. The processing temperature of 65°C for two minutes is sufficient to destroy *Salmonella* species after which the egg is rapidly cooled to 3°C and then tested for the enzyme alpha amylase. Absence of the enzyme, normally found in raw, untreated egg, identifies that pasteurisation has been adequate.

Sterilisation

Sterilisation destroys all micro-organisms, giving an extended product life. However, true sterilisation is difficult to achieve, so a form of treatment referred to as commercial sterilisation is often used. This process destroys all organisms that are likely to cause food poisoning or spoilage, but it also changes the flavour and texture of food and reduces the nutritional value including the loss of vitamins.

Commercial sterilisation is achieved by heating food to a temperature above 100°C usually by steam under pressure. For example, milk is heated at a temperature of 100°C for 30 minutes, followed by a two-stage cooling process. Sterilised products such as milk do not have to be refrigerated until they have been opened.

Ohmic heating is a method of commercially sterilising sauces containing small pieces that can be pumped – for example, minced beef sauce for a cottage pie – using an electric current. Once heated, the food is packed in aseptic conditions into sterile containers.

Ultra heat treatment (UHT)

This technique was developed to give a long shelf life to food without substantially changing its texture or flavour. Milk is heated to 132°C for one second before being filled aseptically into sterile packaging. Products treated in this way do not have to be refrigerated until they have been opened.

Canning

In this form of heat treatment, food is placed in a can that is sealed then treated so that all particles of food reach a temperature of 121°C for at least three minutes. If a large can of dense food is being treated, the process could involve heating for 45 minutes. This is called a 'botulinum cook' because the process destroys the heat resistant spores of the bacterium *Clostridium botulinum*.

Other combinations of time and temperature can be used to achieve the same effect and all canned foods have long shelf lives, limited only by the slow chemical and physical changes that may take place in the food.

Canning – heating food to 121°C for at least three minutes

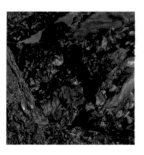

Dehydration preserves food by reducing a_w

Dehydration

Dehydration preserves food by reducing the amount of water available to bacteria, yeasts and moulds. The availability of water is expressed as water activity (a_w). Most bacteria need an a_w of at least 0.95 and very few can exist at an a_w of 0.6. Dried food usually contains less than 25 % moisture and has an a_w of less than 0.6. Yeasts and moulds can normally grow at a lower a_w than bacteria. (For additional information on a_w *see* page 20.)

Some bacteria, such as *Clostridium perfringens*, survive dehydration by forming spores that become active when food is reconstituted.

Dehydration can be achieved by:

- sun drying – for example, for currants and figs
- artificial drying – normally quicker and more effective than sun drying, so used for most packaged convenience foods.

Artificial drying includes:

- hot air – for example, spray drying, roller drying and tunnel drying
- warm air – for example, accelerated freeze drying.

Spray drying of milk involves spraying pasteurised milk into a stream of hot air. Moisture from the milk droplets is lost resulting in the formation of a powder. In roller drying a food paste is spread over a heated roller or drum. As water is lost, the dried food is scraped off the drum. Drying of fruit and vegetables is usually carried out in a tunnel drier. Product is continually moved through a tunnel of hot air until it is sufficiently dry to be stable. In this process vegetables need to be blanched before drying to stop enzyme activity during storage.

In accelerated freeze drying the product is frozen quickly and then heated in a vacuum. Ice that initially formed in the food turns to vapour and is extracted leaving the dehydrated product. Instant coffee can be produced by this process.

Hot air drying denatures the protein in the food so that the texture and flavour are significantly affected. Accelerated freeze drying affects food cells less so the product may be reconstituted with little change in flavour and appearance.

Chemical preservation

Salt

Salt has been used as a preservative for centuries. It is used in curing, brining and pickling to preserve food and enhance its flavour. The preservative effect of salt is partly due to osmosis. In simple terms, the salt absorbs the water making it unavailable to bacteria or moulds.

Some bacteria can grow in salt, while others survive but cannot multiply. *Salmonella* will grow in an 8% concentration. *Staphylococci* can tolerate relatively high salt concentrations of up to 20% and can multiply in these conditions with little competition from other bacteria. As a result *Staphylococci* are often associated with outbreaks of food poisoning from meats that have been partly preserved using salt. Cured canned meats are usually pasteurised but not highly salted, so they must be stored under refrigeration.

Sugar

Sugar, which is used to preserve condensed milk, some cakes, candied fruit, jam and some other conserves, acts in a similar way to salt but the concentration of sugar needs to be approximately six times higher to achieve the same effect. Moulds and yeasts can survive stronger sugar concentrations than most bacteria because they do not need as much moisture. Problems of mould growth can occur when the sugar content of jam is reduced and other preservatives are removed. It is usually recommended that such jams (or conserves) are refrigerated after opening to reduce this risk.

Pickling

Bacteria will not multiply below pH 4.5. Bacterial spores will survive below pH 4.5 but will only germinate above pH 4.5. Therefore, acidifying suitable foods – for example, onions, gherkins – in vinegar (acetic acid) that has a pH of approximately 3, creates these conditions and preserves the food.

Nitrates and nitrites

Sodium nitrate and sodium nitrite are both widely used in the curing of meat. In addition to stabilising the colour of red meat, they inhibit food poisoning organisms (in particular *Clostridium* species) and some organisms that cause spoilage.

Proprionic acid

Sodium or calcium propionates are very effective mould inhibitors and are widely used as additives in bread, cakes and cheeses.

Salt, sugar and vinegar are commonly used for preserving food

Physical preservation

Adjusting the atmosphere

The proportion of oxygen in the air around a food is reduced so that spoilage micro-organisms can only grow very slowly. Generally air is either removed (vacuum packing) or replaced (modified atmosphere packaging). To achieve a satisfactory extension of shelf life, food in such packaging must also be refrigerated.

With **vacuum packing** the product is placed in an appropriate plastic bag and the air is pulled out by machine and the bag is sealed. In this way most oxygen is removed and, as long as the product is refrigerated, the growth of spoilage organisms is slowed down and shelf life extended. Bacon is often packed this way as it is also very effective in reducing oxidative rancidity in the fat present.

In **modified atmosphere packaging (MAP)** the air is replaced by a mixture of usually high levels of nitrogen and carbon dioxide. The effect of reduced oxygen works in the same way as in vacuum packing and, as long as the product is refrigerated, a much longer shelf life is possible.

Smoking

The preservative effect of smoking is partly due to dehydration. Moulds and some types of bacteria, such as *Clostridium botulinum*, may survive, particularly if there is a low concentration of salt. Smoked foods should be kept as indicated on the label, usually refrigerated.

LEAFY SALAD WITH TATSOI

MILD

Physical preservation techniques include vacuum packaging, MAP and smoking

Legal considerations

Food must not be allowed to become contaminated and measures must be taken to prevent this at all stages of preservation. Specific regulations provide detailed standards for the processing and preservation of certain foods – such as milk and pasteurised egg – and for the amounts of additives allowed in various types of food.

Examples of supervisory management

- Supervisors with responsibility for preservation should ensure that the correct methods are carried out at all stages of the process.
- Supervisors with responsibility for the use of preserved foods and ingredients should ensure that manufacturers' instructions are followed for use, storage conditions and shelf-life.

Chapter 10
Storage and temperature

Food is stored to ensure adequate provisions and to prevent fluctuations in supply and demand. Bulk food storage is usually cheaper and more convenient than daily purchase and storage, although fresh perishable produce is usually supplied every day or every other day. Correct storage is essential for a hygienic and efficient food business because the rate of food spoilage is affected by temperature, humidity, stock rotation practices and the integrity of packaging.

Potential hazards

- **Bacterial contamination** – most raw food carries micro-organisms. Spoilage and pathogenic bacteria, moulds and yeasts may be present in food.
- **Bacterial multiplication** – unsatisfactory storage conditions allow micro-organisms to multiply quickly.
- **Food pests** – stored product pests carried into premises in packaged food, or an infestation resulting from unsatisfactory storage conditions.
- **Cross-contamination** – from raw and high-risk food stored close together, from raw food stored above high risk food, or from pest infestation.
- **Physical contamination** – from people, pests in food, storage units in poor condition, or nuts, bolts and similar items from badly-maintained machinery and equipment.
- **Chemical contamination** – storing chemicals next to food or in inappropriate containers.

Stock rotation

Stock rotation is important to maintain the correct levels of stock needed and to ensure that older food is used first, thereby reducing spoilage. All types of food should be rotated. Daily checks should be made on short-life, perishable food but weekly examinations may suffice for other types of food.

Effective stock rotation also assists pest control – areas are disturbed where rodents and insects might otherwise be harboured. In addition, staff can carry out visual checks for infestation and clean thoroughly.

Stock should be checked at regular intervals and rotated

Date marking goods helps to ensure effective stock rotation

Date marks

Date marking goods helps to ensure that stock is rotated effectively. The dates are based on the minimum shelf life of food – the period of time when food is expected to be just as the manufacturer intended, provided it is stored properly. Some companies also use their own date code or colour code to help them to rotate stock correctly.

Use by

Highly perishable foods that often become a food safety risk – high-risk foods such as ready meals, sandwiches, cooked meat – must carry a use-by date in the form of the:

- day and month

or

- day, month and year.

It is illegal to sell food at any time after its use-by date or to alter the date unless you have the manufacturer's permission.

A label should also tell you about the ideal storage conditions for keeping food safe for the storage period – foods with a use-by date generally require refrigeration.

Best before

This type of date mark indicates when food is at its best quality. It is applicable to most foods other than highly perishable ones. The best-before date mark must be shown either as:

- the day, month and year

or

- best before end, followed by the month and year, or just the year.

The year does not have to be included when the food will remain at its best for only three months or less. The day may be omitted if the food will remain at its best for more than three months.

Foods without a date mark

Some foods are exempt from labelling requirements. These include:

- fresh fruit and vegetables, provided that they have not been peeled or cut into pieces
- most alcoholic drinks (beer must have a date mark)
- confectionery made with flour and bread normally eaten within 24 hours of being made
- vinegar
- cooking salt
- solid sugar and products made from flavoured or coloured sugars
- chewing gum and similar products
- edible ices.

Some foods do not require date marks – for example, wine and fresh-baked bread

Receiving a delivery of food

Procedures will vary depending on the particular product, or products, involved but might include:

- checking that the food conforms to the agreed product specification (see page 64)
- checking the cleanliness of the delivery vehicle and personnel – is the vehicle refrigerated to the correct temperature if carrying high risk foods?
- inspecting the condition of deliveries immediately upon their arrival, checking date coding, condition of food and wrapping, and temperatures and rejecting if the condition of the food or its packaging is not up to standard
- unless stated otherwise on the operators' specification, rejecting frozen food if it is delivered at a temperature above -10°C and rejecting refrigerated food if it has a temperature above 8°C
- following company procedures – for example, putting the company's date coding on food prior to storage
- placing food in the appropriate store as soon as possible
- separating unfit food and labelling it as unfit
- storing chemicals in separate storage areas away from food.

Check food on delivery

Damaged food

All food should be inspected for damage:

- on arrival
- during storage
- just before it is to be used.

The examination may be:

- organoleptic – by sight, smell, feel, taste and even by sound (for instance, when bread is tapped)
- according to the company's specifications for bacteria, appearance or weight
- by mould, bacterial or chemical analysis.

Damaged stock must be kept apart and clearly marked so that it is not used in error. Ideally it should be stored in a separate designated area. Its disposal should be in a manner – such as crushing or dyeing the food – that eliminates the possibility of resale.

Check food before use

Product identification and traceability

Product identification and traceability systems are vital in most food operations and supervisors are generally going to be involved both in their implementation and control. They are particularly important in large catering businesses – for example, in cook-chill and cook-freeze operations that are covered in this chapter (see pages 71–74) – and in the manufacturing and retail sectors where food, once it has been produced, may be widely distributed.

In situations where there is a specific problem with a food product that means it must be removed from sale, or recalled, effective methods of identifying and tracing that product are essential. It is also important within a food safety management system to be able to trace batches of ingredients, work-in-progress or finished products, so that in the event of a failure at a critical control point (see page 120) ingredients or products that need to be rejected can be identified and isolated.

In a retail situation, packaged foods can be identified by either their 'use-by' or 'best-before' dates. When stock deliveries arrive, sample date codes should be checked to ensure that products are in code and that they have sufficient shelf life remaining to allow them to be displayed and sold.

To assist in the event of a product recall, the Food (Lot Marking) Regulations 1996 require that pre-packed foods be identified with a batch or 'lot' number. The size of a batch and the choice of number are both generally up to the producer, manufacturer, packager or first seller as long as the lot number is easily visible, clearly legible and indelible.

For loose products, such as meat items, displayed on a delicatessen counter or those manufactured in store, a system is required to ensure that products are rotated on a 'first-in-first-out' basis and, that in the situation where a product is recalled, they can be clearly identified. Therefore, dates of arrival or production can be marked on boxes or individual ticketing together with the period of display. Colour stickers or product books can also be used, provided the system is understood by staff.

In manufacturing operations, identification and traceability procedures need to be maintained and relevant information recorded at all stages of production – from the purchase and receipt of raw materials, storage, batch assembly, processing and packaging, through to the storage and distribution of the finished product.

Pre-packed food must be identified with a batch number

Product specifications

In food manufacturing operations, raw materials are generally purchased from approved suppliers against agreed specifications that detail minimum acceptable standards. The same is generally the case when major retailers purchase own-label products from manufacturers. Product specifications usually include the following information:

- name and address of the supplier
- description of the raw material or product and, if appropriate, what it is used for
- chemical name or ingredient list
- agreed microbiological standards and tolerances
- any specific factors with tolerance limits – for example, pH, salt, permitted additives
- agreed analytical data – for example, fat content, calories, pesticide residues
- storage conditions
- shelf life
- safe handling procedures and instructions for use
- labelling requirements
- batch identification details.

For high-risk raw materials and finished products where suppliers are generally audited before being accepted, processing information and details of the HACCP plan (*see* Chapter 15) are normally required as part of the specification.

Certificates of analysis may be provided for individual batches of a raw material or product to confirm that any specific criteria agreed in the specification have been met – for example, microbiological standards such as the total viable count, absence of *Salmonella* or analytical data such as fat content or the absence of specific additives.

Supervisors are generally involved in ensuring that agreed specifications are met and, in some situations, this might include their involvement in the control of both incoming raw materials from suppliers and the manufacture of own-label products for customers.

Dry goods stores should be clean and tidy, well lit and ventilated

Storage

Dry food stores

- Dry food stores need to be dry, cool, of adequate size and pest proof.

- All food should be covered to reduce risk of contamination – this may involve the use of lidded, pest proof containers.

- Adequate lighting is necessary to aid cleaning and the detection of pests.

- There must be an effective ventilation system because temperature fluctuations can lead to condensation, which may lead to food spoilage or cause contamination. Mechanical systems are more efficient than opening and closing windows.

- Food should be stored off the floor on shelving, mobile bins or pallets so that an effective cleaning schedule can be followed.

- Chemicals, including those used for cleaning, or strong smelling non-food items that could taint – such as perfumed soaps or household cleaning agents that may be stored in retail outlets – should not be held in dry food storage areas.

Guidelines for handling canned foods

Canned foods should be stored in dry, cool, well-ventilated conditions. They should be examined on delivery and marked with the date. Once stored, they should be checked regularly and the principles of stock rotation followed (*see* page 61). Canned food should be rejected if the can is blown, dented, rusted, holed or showing signs of seam damage, or if the contents are the wrong texture or have an unusual smell or colour. Once cans are opened the contents should be used immediately or the contents transferred to plastic or stainless steel containers, which should be covered and refrigerated. Containers should also be identified with a date indicating when the contents were transferred and by when they should be used (or a similar appropriate coding system). Manufacturer's recommendations should be followed when deciding how long to store such food. If there is any doubt, it should be used on the same day or discarded.

Refrigerators

Refrigerators only delay food spoilage by bacteria and moulds, they do not prevent it. Most common food poisoning organisms cannot multiply or produce toxins at temperatures below 5°C. However, certain pathogens, such as *Listeria* and *Clostridium botulinum*, do multiply slowly at temperatures below 5°C.

Refrigerators should operate at a temperature between 1°C and 4°C. Domestic refrigerators are not usually suitable for commercial usage because they do not stay cold enough when the doors are opened frequently.

The hygienic and efficient use of refrigerated storage units depends upon a number of factors.

Prevention of contamination

- Raw and high-risk foods must be kept apart and ideally separate refrigerators should be used. If this is not possible, raw food must be stored below cooked food.
- All food should be adequately covered to protect it from contamination and prevent it from drying out, absorbing odours or causing contamination.
- Acidic food should not be refrigerated in opened cans because the acid can attack the internal surface of the can.

Siting

Refrigerators should be:

- easy to access for storing and retrieving food and cleaning the surrounding area and the refrigerant coils
- positioned away from any heat source
- positioned in a well-ventilated area away from the direct rays of the sun

Large refrigerator motors should be installed outside the building or outside the food area as they generate heat and dust.

Maintenance and cleaning

- Refrigerators should be constructed so that they are easy to maintain and clean.
- They should be maintained in a good condition and serviced regularly.
- Door seals should be checked regularly to ensure that they do not perish and become difficult to clean.
- Damage to the internal or external cladding may allow moisture into the insulation, which will affect the efficiency of the refrigerator.
- A suitable sanitiser should be used to clean all internal surfaces, which must then be dried thoroughly.
- Chiller and refrigerator door handles should be cleaned and disinfected as part of a cleaning schedule.
- Spills should be cleared up immediately.

Loading

- Refrigerators must not be overloaded as good air circulation is necessary to keep a constant temperature.
- Efficiency is impaired if food is placed in front of the cooling unit.
- Hot food should be cooled rapidly before storing. If the food is still warm when it is refrigerated, the temperature inside the refrigerator may rise, increasing the possibility of bacterial multiplication. Condensation may also form and drip onto other food with the risk of causing contamination. Such conditions will also encourage the formation of mould.

Defrosting

- If refrigerated units do not defrost automatically, defrosting should be carried out regularly and in accordance with manufacturer's instructions.
- When ice builds up, it increases the cost of maintaining the correct temperature.

Refrigerated display cabinets are designed to hold food at a specific temperature

Display freezers should not be loaded above the load line

Refrigerated display cabinets

Refrigerated display cabinets are designed to hold temperatures at a particular level and not to cool product down and, for this reason, it is important that checks are made on deliveries and on the product before it is loaded into the cabinet. Products should be loaded into the cabinet to allow good air circulation and it must not be positioned beyond load lines.

As with any refrigeration unit correct positioning is important. The following could all affect their efficiency:

- warm air from heaters or other equipment
- restricted air flow to compressors
- draughts, especially across open displays
- radiant energy – such as from direct sunlight or lamps.

Freezers

The temperature for a domestic-type freezer should be between -18°C and -25°C, but commercial freezers may be colder. Food must be well wrapped to prevent freezer burn occurring through loss of moisture. Air does not need to circulate so food can be stored close together. Display freezers must not be loaded above the load line and temperatures for all freezers must be checked regularly. In the event of a freezer breakdown there should be a procedure in place and the environmental health practitioner may advise on the safe disposal of the food.

Thawing frozen food

Some food can be cooked straight from the freezer, but joints of meat, poultry and other large items must be thawed before cooking. The manufacturer's instructions must always be followed. If frozen food is not thawed completely, ice crystals remain at the centre. Although the cooking will melt the ice, the internal temperature may not be hot enough to destroy all the pathogenic micro-organisms.

Food must be thawed carefully to ensure that there is no bacterial contamination from the thawed liquid. When small refrigerators are used for thawing and storing at the same time, the stored food can easily become contaminated. If food is thawed at an ambient temperature, bacteria will start to multiply rapidly on the surface of the food while the centre remains frozen or is still thawing.

Ideally, food should be thawed in a specially designed thawing cabinet or a cool place. The thawing food should be protected from contamination and should not be able to contaminate other foods, such as ready-to-eat foods. Once food is thawed, it should either be cooked immediately, or it should be refrigerated until it is cooked or consumed.

Cooked food

If cooked food is not required for immediate consumption after cooking, it must be:

■ kept at a temperature of 63°C or above

or

■ cooled rapidly and then put into a refrigerator or chilled area.

If cooked food is cooled, it should reach a temperature of 5°C or below as quickly as possible (ideally within one to two hours). Food cools more rapidly if cool air can circulate around it. Blast chillers are generally designed to reduce the temperature of cooked foods from 70°C to 3°C in less than 90 minutes. To enable this temperature change to occur, cooked foods should be portioned into shallow trays (such as many ready-meals), joints of raw meat should be portioned to weigh less than 2.5 kg (about 5 lb), and large volumes of hot liquids (such as soups, stews, gravies or sauces) should be poured into shallow pans or trays before cooling. (Also *see* section on cook-chill on page 71.)

Thaw frozen food carefully

Cool cooked food as quickly as possible

Temperature measuring equipment

The four main types of temperature measuring equipment are:

- simple in-place devices
- automatic air temperature monitoring systems
- electronic probe thermometers
- infra-red thermometers.

Because of the risk of breakage and contamination of foods, glass thermometers should not be permitted in any areas where open food is handled.

Simple in-place devices

These may range from self-adhesive liquid crystal display strips to dial or digital thermometers that are built into refrigeration units. They measure air temperature and, therefore, only give an approximate indication of product temperature. They are often positioned to indicate the temperature in the warmest part of the unit and, for this purpose, they are reasonable monitoring devices.

Automatic air temperature monitoring systems

These systems monitor temperature continuously and are fitted with sensors that are wired back to a central control – for example, sensors fitted into display cabinets in retail outlets to sensors fitted to walk-in refrigeration units in a manufacturing facility. An alarm will be triggered if temperatures exceed target levels. They are effective in that they provide constant temperature monitoring and allow an immediate response to any faults. Additionally they usually provide printed records, which can form part of a due diligence defence.

Electronic probe thermometers

Electronic probe thermometers are usually fitted with a solid metal probe located at its tip and linked to an electronic unit with a digital display. However, a variety of alternative probes can be fitted – for example special flat probes can be used for testing between packs.

They are widely used, in particular for:

- checking food temperatures of food in fridges or on display
- checking the core (the centre of the thickest part of the food) temperatures of foods during cooking, cooling and reheating
- checking temperatures of food deliveries
- confirming air temperatures in refrigerators and freezers.

They must be calibrated and checked on a regular basis. Probe thermometers can be checked at:

- 0°C – agitate the probe in a mixture of ice and a small amount of water until a steady reading is achieved. It should be within the range -1°C to +1°C otherwise the unit should be repaired.
- 100°C – agitate the probe in boiling water until a steady reading is achieved. It should be within the range 99°C to 101°C otherwise the unit should be repaired.

Particular care must be taken to ensure that the probes themselves do not cause contamination – probes should be cleaned and disinfected after use with raw foods and before use with ready-to-eat foods.

Infra-red thermometers

Infra-red thermometers, which detect radiant energy, give rapid temperature measurements of product surfaces and are very effective for screening deliveries or food in display cabinets.

Staff need to be trained in their use otherwise readings taken may be unreliable – for example, if the thermometer is just pointed at food from a distance it may also detect and measure the temperature of other items and not just the temperature of the food being checked.

Any deviations found when using infra-red thermometers are usually checked and confirmed with an electronic probe thermometer.

Taking temperature readings

Taking air temperatures

Whether reading a sensor fitted in the refrigeration unit or using a hand-held probe it is important to be aware that air temperature may not be the same as food temperature. Also air temperatures may vary. Readings taken within an hour of a defrost cycle will not be reliable or if the door has been left open in a walk-in unit. In some units, the temperature may vary depending on the point where the temperature is taken. For example, in many open display cabinets cold air is circulated and temperature measurements taken at the 'air off' point, where cold air is coming off the refrigeration unit, is likely to be colder than at the 'air in' point where it is being returned from the cabinet back to the refrigeration unit. Also, air temperature readings taken immediately after an open display cabinet has been re-stocked may be misleading.

Taking food temperatures

Direct product testing involves inserting a probe directly into the centre or thickest part of the product. This method is suitable for many situations and the most reliable in terms of getting a product temperature. The probe must be cleaned and disinfected before use and also between use on different products. If taking a reading involves breaking the packaging, the product must be rejected.

To overcome the problem of puncturing packaging, a satisfactory estimate of food temperature can be achieved from 'between pack' testing where a flattened or wire probe is held in close contact between two packs of food. It is not as accurate as direct product testing and a tolerance of about 2°C is usually allowed. It is also important that foods are selected that give good contact and where packaging best allows the temperature of the food to be measured. This method is often used when assessing the efficiency of chill cabinets – for example, products are measured on different shelves and on the base of the cabinet at different times of the day to establish a pattern of operation. This information can then be used to identify the best place in the cabinet to take routine readings that will best indicate that all the food products in the cabinet are being maintained at an acceptable temperature.

Recording temperature checks

Generally, unless temperatures are being recorded continuously, a record should be kept of all routine temperature checks. If the temperature is found to be outside the specified target range, a record should be made of any corrective action taken. Reporting by exception (only keeping a record when there are problems or changes) is considered acceptable for small catering and retail businesses (see page 130). The frequency of checking will vary but, as a guide, refrigerator temperatures should be checked at least on a daily basis.

Direct product testing is the most reliable method for taking temperatures

A record should be kept of all routine temperature checks

Cook-chill
Stages in a cook-chill operation

1. Purchase of raw materials

2. Delivery of raw materials

3. Storage

4. Preparation

5. Cooking

6. Portioning

7. Cooling – blast chilling

8. Storage

9. Distribution

10. Reheating

11. Service

Cook-chill applies to catering operations and, in particular, to meals produced for use in hospitals and other forms of institutional catering, including meals on wheels. However, it can also be applied to commercial catering and, in many respects, it has been adapted to manufacturing operations where many of the same basic principles are followed.

In the institutional model, food is cooked and portioned, followed by rapid chilling and storage at 0°C to +3°C and subsequent thorough reheating close to the consumer before consumption. The product has a maximum shelf life of five days including the day of production and the day of consumption. Food is usually prepared in centralised production units prior to distribution for reheating and prompt consumption.

The basic principles of cook-chill are:

- all raw materials should be of good microbiological quality
- cooking should destroy any vegetative pathogens
- rapid chilling after cooking should control the growth of micro-organisms and in particular the germination of spores and the subsequent multiplication of vegetative pathogens
- cross-contamination should be avoided at all stages and in particular between raw and cooked food
- storage and distribution conditions for the cooked food should ensure its quality and safety
- reheating and service procedures should ensure the food is safe to eat and are crucial to its palatability
- all the above should be closely monitored.

(Source: *Chilled and Frozen – Guidelines on Cook-Chill and Cook-Freeze Catering Systems*, Department of Health, HMSO, 1989)

To achieve all the above cook-chill operations need to adopt systems based on HACCP with essential control checks in place and recorded for every batch and individual menu item processed. This will involve extensive quality and safety checks on raw materials, temperature checks at all stages of the process and procedures in place for stock rotation as well as the design and maintenance of the structure of the premises and equipment (including a clearly defined linear flow), personal hygiene, staff training, cleaning, disinfection and waste disposal and pest control.

Procedures must be in place at each stage of a cook-chill operation to ensure that food safety is maintained.

1. Purchase of raw materials
- All raw materials are to be of good quality and purchased from approved suppliers. This will usually involve suppliers having to conform to agreed specifications following food safety inspections/audits of their premises.

2. Delivery of raw materials
- All raw materials inspected on receipt and checked against an agreed specification before acceptance.

3. Storage
- Prior to use, raw materials should be stored at appropriate temperature and humidity levels to ensure microbial multiplication and any loss of nutrients is kept to a minimum. This should include the provision of suitable facilities for ambient, refrigerated and frozen storage.

4. Preparation
- Raw materials prepared in areas physically separated from cooking and post-cooking areas.
- Restricted movement of staff in raw material preparation areas to prevent the risk of cross contamination.
- Use of separate colour-coded equipment and utensils, particularly knives, for raw and cooked food areas.
- Controlled thawing of frozen raw materials.
- Joints of meat or packs of meat not to exceed 2.5kg in weight and 100mm in thickness or height. Large poultry carcasses to be broken down into sections to conform to these parameters.

To ensure food safety separate raw and cooked food

Cook food to at least 70°C for two minutes

Portion food and label quickly

5. Cooking

- Food cooked to a core temperature of at least 70°C for not less than two minutes (or sufficient to destroy all non-spore-forming pathogens).

6. Portioning

- Portioning of food into smaller quantities, including labelling, must be completed as soon as possible after cooking and take no longer than 30 minutes.

- Food portioned into containers with a depth of no more than 50mm to ensure rapid cooling.

- Wherever possible portioning to be carried out in a controlled environment room with a maximum ambient temperature of 10°C.

7. Cooling – blast chilling

- Portioned food chilled to between 0°C and +3°C within a further 90 minutes (i.e. chilled from cooking to +3°C or below within two hours, including the 30 minutes allowed for portioning).

- Fully loaded chiller units must be capable of reducing the temperature of 50mm layers of food from 70°C to +3°C or below in no more than 90 minutes (this could not be achieved in a storage refrigerator).

8. Storage

- Refrigeration units must be capable of maintaining the products within 0°C to +3°C.

- All containers must be clearly identified and include the date of production and date of expiry.

- The maximum shelf life of the food is five days including the day of production and the day of consumption.

- A strict system of stock rotation must be observed.

- If the temperature of the food exceeds +5°C but not +10°C, it must be eaten within 12 hours (increases in product temperature up to +5°C may be permitted for very short periods of time – for example when on a defrost cycle).

- If the food exceeds +10°C, either in storage or distribution, it must be destroyed.

9. Distribution

- During any stage of distribution the temperature of the food must be maintained between 0°C and +3°C.

10. Reheating

- Reheating of the food must take place no more than 30 minutes after it has been removed from chill and must reach a minimum temperature of 70°C for at least two minutes.

11. Service

- Reheated food must be served within 15 minutes of reheating and it must not be allowed to fall below 63°C.

- Any meals not consumed must be destroyed and not reheated or returned to chilled storage.

Chill to 3°C or below within 90 minutes

Maintain products at 0–3°C

Cook-freeze

The process up to and including portioning is the same as cook-chill. Blast freezing must then bring the core temperature of the food down to at least -5°C within 90 minutes and subsequently must reach a storage temperature of -18°C. Stored at -18°C or below, shelf life will vary according to the type of food and range from two to twelve months. Reheating is as cook-chill but includes safe procedures for thawing. The core temperature of the reheated product must reach at least 70°C for at least two minutes.

Reheat cook-chill and cook-freeze products to 70°C for at least two minutes

Serve reheated food within 15 minutes

Legal considerations

Regulation (EC) No. 852/2004 on the hygiene of foodstuffs applies to all member states in the European Union and sets standards for the construction and maintenance of food storage rooms and equipment as well as stating that food business operators shall put in place, implement, and maintain permanent procedures based on HACCP principles.

The Food Hygiene (England) Regulations 2006, The Food Hygiene (Scotland) Regulations 2005, The Food Hygiene (Wales) Regulations 2006 and The Food Hygiene Regulations (Northern Ireland) 2006 – set temperature control standards for food that is likely to support the multiplication of pathogenic micro-organisms or the formation of toxins.

There is a general requirement that raw foods, ingredients and intermediate and finished products must not be kept at a temperature that would lead to a risk to health.

Apart from some specified exemptions (see page 147), food that is likely to support the multiplication of pathogenic micro-organisms or the formation of toxins must be stored at below 8°C (England, Wales and Northern Ireland) or under refrigeration (Scotland). If such food is to be kept hot, it must be held at 63°C or above (England, Wales, Northern Ireland and Scotland).

Cooked food to be eaten, used or stored cold must be cooled as rapidly as possible.

The Food Labelling Regulations 1996 deal with date marks. Except for a number of exempted products, food must be labelled with an appropriate 'use-by' or 'best-before' date.

The Food (Lot Marking) Regulations 1996 require that pre-packed foods be identified with a batch or lot number to assist in the event of a product recall.

Under the Quick-frozen Food Regulations 1990 quick-frozen food must be date marked and labelled with temperature and storage information. There are legal requirements for monitoring freezer temperatures at the manufacturers and at retail outlets.

Examples of supervisory management

Correct storage is essential for a hygienic and efficient food business – supervisors have a key role to play in this area by:

- setting a good example
- helping to set standards and monitor procedures
- creating or implementing delivery procedures, stock rotation and dating systems, cleaning schedules, temperature monitoring procedures and supplier and/or customer specifications
- communicating standards and procedures to staff
- training staff to recognise signs of spoilage, deal with deliveries and damaged stock, and carry out stock rotation
- ensuring the provision of resources such as materials, equipment, time, date coding machines, temperature probes and monitoring devices
- implementing storage and temperature control procedures
- monitoring a range of records, such as temperatures, delivery and stock, and checking the accuracy of temperature monitoring equipment and suppliers' deliveries against company specifications
- motivating staff to maintain standards by using a variety of approaches such as refresher training, staff meetings, check lists, posters and disciplinary action
- checking (auditing) and reviewing the system
- taking any necessary corrective action.

Chapter 11
Personal hygiene

Food handlers must always observe the highest possible standards of personal hygiene to ensure that food does not become contaminated by microbiological, physical, chemical or allergenic contaminants. High standards of personal hygiene play an important part in creating a good public image while protecting food and helping to ensure legal compliance.

Potential hazards

- **Bacterial contamination** – particularly *Staphylococcus aureus*, from septic cuts, hands, hair, the nose or mouth.
- **Cross-contamination** – involving bacteria including types of *Salmonella* and *Campylobacter* – from unwashed hands that touch raw then high risk foods.
- **Carriers** – whether healthy or convalescent.
- **Physical contamination** – from jewellery, hair or fingernails, etc.
- **Chemical contamination** – from perfume, scented soaps or aftershaves, etc.
- **Allergenic contamination** – from unwashed hands that touch allergens and then prepare food that is supposed to be allergen-free.

Hand hygiene

About 15% of adults carry *Staphylococcus aureus* on their skin. Food handlers must wash their hands regularly throughout the working day to reduce the number of bacteria on their skin and to prevent cross-contamination. In particular, they must wash their hands:

- before entering a food preparation area
- between handling raw and high-risk food
- after taking a break
- after going to the toilet
- after eating, smoking, sneezing into a tissue, blowing their nose or touching any other part of the body
- after handling waste food or refuse.

Apart from setting a good example, supervisors need to be aware of other bad habits that can lead to the possible contamination of food and to take appropriate action. For example:

- using fingers to taste food
- using the same spoon to taste different foods
- licking fingers to help separate food packaging materials
- blowing into bags to open them
- breathing onto glasses or cutlery when polishing them
- biting nails or sucking fingers.

To prevent chemical contamination, food handlers must wash their hands after using cleaning chemicals and, to prevent allergenic contamination, after handling known allergens.

It is vital in food operations, and especially where open food is prepared, that hands are not only washed regularly but also that they are washed thoroughly. This is often overlooked and in the worst situation ignored (*see* diagram opposite).

An important part of a supervisors' role to ensure that thorough hand washing procedures are observed, in particular:

- use hot running water – ideally 45–50°C.
- wet hands before applying unperfumed, bactericidal liquid soap
- rub hands vigorously for about 15 to 20 seconds ensuring that, both sides of hands are washed and, particular attention is paid washing thumbs, between fingers, fingertips and under nails
- rinse hands under running water
- dry hands thoroughly using a clean dry paper towel (bacteria will spread more easily if hands are wet).

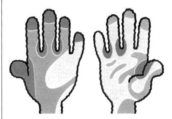

Food handlers must wash their hands thoroughly

- ◼ Areas frequently missed during hand washing
- ◼ Less frequently missed
- Not usually missed

Always use a hand basin provided exclusively for washing hands

Use comfortably hot water, rub your hands vigorously to work in the soap

Don't forget the areas between your fingers and around your wrists

Rinse your hands before drying them

Hot air dryers and one-use pull-through type towels may be suitable for hand drying in some situations, but are not recommended where open food is handled. They pose a contamination risk if hands are not thoroughly dried (as often happens with hot air dryers) or the towel roll comes to an end or is not moved on (in the case of pull-through towel dispensers).

A nail brush can be used to clean fingernails. It must be cleaned and disinfected frequently and always at the end of the working day, then left to air dry. Disposable or plastic nail brushes with nylon bristles are recommended.

Fingernails should always be short, clean and unvarnished as nail varnish inhibits cleaning, harbours dirt and bacteria and may chip and contaminate food. For the same reason nail extensions should not be permitted.

People who bite their fingernails create a further hazard as they run the risk of transferring *Staphylococcus aureus* from their mouth to their hands, then to food. This is an important area to take into account when considering whether or not to employ food handlers.

Cuts, boils, septic spots and skin infections

Staff with septic cuts or boils, especially if they cannot be adequately covered with an appropriate waterproof dressing, should be excluded from food handling areas as they are likely to be carrying *Staphylococcus aureus*.

Uninfected cuts should be covered by a clean, easy-to-detect, waterproof dressing. All dressings must be waterproof to prevent blood and bacteria from the cut contaminating food and also to prevent bacteria, especially from raw food, from infecting the cut and making it septic. Dressings should also be highly visible – they are usually blue, a non-food colour – so that they may be seen and recovered if dropped in food. Waterproof dressings specifically for food use contain a thin metal strip allowing detection of lost dressings in food production situations where metal detectors are used. Lost dressings must be reported immediately. Staff must have access to adequate first aid facilities, including detectable waterproof dressings.

Skin infections such as dermatitis, eczema and psoriasis may increase the possibility of food contamination. People with these conditions may need to be excluded from food handling duties.

Uninfected cuts should be covered by a clean, easy-to-detect, waterproof dressing

Food handlers should not wear any jewellery

Jewellery

Food handlers should not wear any jewellery because it harbours dirt and bacteria and could cause physical contamination if jewellery or gemstones fall into food. (There is also a risk of entrapment if food handlers wear jewellery while operating machinery.) Some companies allow staff to wear a plain wedding ring and specific arrangements may be necessary for jewellery worn for religious or cultural reasons.

Scented personal hygiene and grooming products

Strongly scented soap, perfume, aftershave and deodorants may taint food and, therefore, should not be used.

The mouth, nose and throat

About 40 % of adults carry *Staphylococcus aureus* in their nose and throat. If food handlers eats while they are working, they are likely to transfer the bacteria from their mouths to their fingers, then to food or utensils. Eating should be prohibited in food areas. If food handlers have to check the taste of food, they must use a clean spoon. If a second or subsequent taste test is necessary, clean spoons must be used each time to prevent contamination of the food.

Coughing and sneezing may spread *Staphylococcus aureus* bacteria by air-borne droplets – anyone with a bad cold and/or sore throat should not handle open food.

Smoking tobacco may induce coughing. Its use must be banned while staff are handling open food or are present in areas where there is open food. Physical contamination may occur if cigarette ends or ash fall into the food. Bacterial contamination may occur if staff touch their lips while smoking or when a saliva-contaminated cigarette end is placed on a work surface. In many food businesses smoking is either restricted to isolated, designated smoking areas or it is totally prohibited. If individuals leave food premises to smoke, they must ensure that they change out of their protective clothing and into their own outdoor clothing before leaving the premises and change back into their protective clothing and wash their hands thoroughly before re-entering food handling areas.

Hair

Staphylococcus aureus and other pathogenic micro-organisms may be found in hair. To protect food from contamination by loose hairs and dandruff, food handlers should wash their hair regularly and keep it completely enclosed by a suitable head covering – which may include a hair net and hat – while working in a food area. Food handlers must not be allowed to comb their hair or adjust hats when they are wearing protective clothing or are in food areas.

Clothing

Special overclothing, including hats, is worn to safeguard food from contamination. Although the clothing may protect the staff's own clothes, this is incidental to the main purpose – the protection of food. Everyone working in a food handling area must wear clean clothing and, where appropriate, must wear protective clothing. Protective clothing may include additional items such as overalls, disposable or washable aprons, boots, rubber, chain-mail or disposable gloves.

Protective clothing should cover the food handlers' own clothes and should be:

- clean
- washable or disposable
- light coloured
- without external pockets.

Any buttons must be securely attached. Hygiene specialists prefer clothing with press studs or strips of quick-release fastening material because there is less risk that they will fall off into food and cause physical contamination.

Outdoor clothing must not be brought into food areas, but should be left in a locker or cloakroom provided for the purpose. Overclothing must not be worn outside the food premises or for travelling to and from work.

In food premises where specific low- and high-risk areas are physically separated (for example, a factory processing and packing both raw and cooked chicken portions) areas are provided for changing into completely different protective clothing and footwear, which may be a different colour, if moving from one area to another.

Food handlers should wear protective clothing including suitable head covering

Exclusion of food handlers

The law states that people should not be permitted to work in food handling areas when:

- they are suffering, or suspected to be suffering, from a disease that could be transmitted through food (or they are carriers)

and

- they could contaminate food with pathogenic micro-organisms, either directly or indirectly, as a result of their work activities.

The code of practice *Food Handling – Fitness to Work* (issued in 1995 by the Department of Health) provides guidance on when people can return to work after sickness or diarrhoea resulting from a common cause of gastro-intestinal infection, such as:

- *Salmonella* species (non-typhoid fever *Salmonellae*), *Campylobacter* species, *Shigella* species, *Bacillus* species, *Staphylococcus aureus* and *Clostridium perfringens*
- viruses
- protozoa or worms.

In general, staff may return to work only when they have been free from vomiting or diarrhoea for 48 hours once any treatment has ceased.

If a member of staff is a confirmed case of typhoid or paratyphoid, there should be six negative faecal samples before a return to work. When the cause of infection is a verocytotoxin-producing *Escherichia coli* (as *E. coli* O157), the staff member must be excluded from work until 48 hours after the symptoms have cleared and there have been two negative faecal samples taken 48 hours apart.

If a food handler has a scaling, weeping or discharging lesion on an exposed part of their skin (face, neck, hands, arms or scalp) they must not work with food until the lesion has healed. This would also apply to weeping or pustular lesions of the eyes, ears, mouth and gums. Clean lesions on exposed skin, such as cuts, must be totally covered with a distinctly-coloured waterproof dressing if an individual is to continue handling food.

Visitors

Hygiene rules relating to the food business should also apply to any visitors to food areas – this could apply to customers, suppliers, maintenance engineers, cleaning contractors, pest control contractors, as well as company staff who do not normally visit food areas. They should be provided with appropriate protective clothing, and other rules such as those relating to jewellery or the wearing of suitable waterproof dressings on cuts should also be complied with. They may be asked to sign that they have read and understood the company hygiene rules and also to complete a medical questionnaire, especially if they are going into areas where open high-risk foods are being prepared.

Customers in retail outlets

Open foods on retail food counters are particularly susceptible to contamination by customers. Visible barriers including sneeze guards are widely used to reduce this risk. Self-service areas for salads are becoming common in some supermarkets and pose a significant risk of bacterial and physical contamination and cross-contamination. These areas need constant staff supervision to check contents and containers and change tongs or spoons (long-handled implements should be supplied, one for each container).

Legal considerations

Regulation (EC) No. 852/2004 on the hygiene of foodstuffs relating specifically to personal hygiene states that:

- People working in food handling areas must maintain a high degree of personal cleanliness and must work in a hygienic manner.

- Food handlers must wear clean overclothing and, where appropriate, wear protective clothing.

- People who work in any food handling area must inform the proprietor of the food business if they know or suspect that they have, or are carrying, a food-borne illness. Similarly, they must report illnesses such as diarrhoea, an infected wound, skin infection, or any other condition that could result in food becoming contaminated by pathogenic micro-organisms. (Anyone who is afflicted with such illnesses or symptoms, or who is a suspected carrier, may be excluded from food handling areas.)

- Proprietors of a food business must ensure that food handlers are supervised, instructed and/or trained in food hygiene matters commensurate with their work activities.

- Food premises must have adequate flush lavatories that do not lead directly into food rooms and hand washing facilities with hot and cold, or appropriately mixed, running water, together with materials for cleaning and drying hands hygienically.

- Food premises must also have a similar and adequate number of suitably located hand washing facilities, which are separate from food washing.

- Where necessary, adequate staff changing facilities must be provided.

Food handlers should be clean and tidy

Food handlers must report illness

Food handlers must be properly supervised

Examples of supervisory management

In any food business a supervisor has a key role to play in ensuring that high standards of personal hygiene are maintained throughout the workforce under his/her control. Depending on the size of the business and the number of staff supervised, some or all of the following examples will apply:

- setting a good personal example
- helping to establish and communicate policy and procedures on a range of issues such as jewellery, exclusion from work and clothing for food handlers
- monitoring staff's personal hygiene and habits, including: visual checks for jewellery, loose hair, incorrectly worn clothing and hand washing thoroughness, arranging for swab testing of hands or recording the results of laboratory tests on faecal samples
- explaining hygiene policies during interviews for new staff or during induction training
- arranging instruction and/or training at induction and basic levels, on a day-to-day basis and as refresher training, emphasising issues such as hand washing, bad habits, reporting sickness, jewellery, clothing policies and individual responsibility
- implementing policies and procedures for personal hygiene
- ensuring the provision of necessary and appropriate resources, such as hand washing facilities, the cleaning and storage of overclothing and the supply of waterproof plasters

- motivating staff to maintain standards by a variety of appropriate approaches, such as refresher training, staff meetings, check lists, posters and , if necessary, disciplinary action
- implementing and monitoring sickness reporting and exclusion procedures
- monitoring a range of records and practices, including the health questionnaires of potential new employees, the records of swabbing and faecal samples and staff behaviour
- checking (auditing) and reviewing procedures and, where appropriate, taking corrective action
- reporting to higher management on personal hygiene issues that could affect food safety.

Chapter 12
Design and construction

The appropriate design and construction of premises and equipment help food businesses maintain high standards of food safety. Good design enables different work activities to be kept apart and makes it easy for staff to clean – both important ways to prevent cross-contamination.

Potential hazards

- **Bacterial contamination** – when there is harbourage for bacteria or food pests or both.
- **Cross-contamination** – when the same surfaces and equipment are used for raw and high-risk foods and are not properly cleaned, or the layout allows cross-over in the preparation and processing of raw and high-risk foods.
- **Physical contamination** – when nuts, bolts, glass or other items fall from machinery, equipment or light fittings.
- **Chemical contamination** – when an incorrect type of food-contact surface is chosen. For instance, some metals, such as zinc and copper, react with acidic foods creating taint and food poisoning.

Site selection

The selection of a suitable site depends on a variety of factors and these will vary depending on the nature of the business. A major consideration for a restaurant may be selecting a location that will attract customers, whereas for a manufacturing unit producing ready meals for major retailers it may be the availability of a suitable workforce or access for delivery and distribution.

All businesses must consider essential services such as a supply of potable water, gas, electricity and waste disposal. Other questions may relate to potential pollution or contamination risks from the immediate environment – for example from smoke, dust, odour, chemicals, pests or flooding. Conversely, food business operators may have to consider whether or not the business is likely to create potential problems – for example from smell, noise or traffic, if located in, or near to, a residential area.

Good design principles

Cross-contamination should be made physically impossible by segregating:

- raw foods from high-risk foods
- clean processes from dirty processes
- the unpacking of containers from food preparation and production areas
- refuse storage from food preparation and production areas.

The design should provide for a continuous linear workflow. Work should flow from the raw to the finished product, with high-risk food kept out of ambient temperatures as much as possible. Other essential design features should include the provision of adequate:

- facilities for personal hygiene, with wash hand basins conveniently positioned near work stations or at entrances to food preparation areas
- means to control temperature at all stages of work
- access to all parts of the premises, including yards and refuse areas, to enable thorough cleaning and disinfection to be carried out
- pest infestation prevention – all pests must be denied access by the use of fly screens, self-closing doors, air curtains and similar measures
- cloakroom and staff facilities – such as cloakrooms with lockers and first aid facilities.

Design should provide for continuous workflow

Construction of food premises

Floors

Floor surfaces should be easy to clean and, where necessary, to disinfect. They should be constructed of materials that will ensure an impervious, non-absorbent, non-toxic and non-slip finish. Depending on use, surfaces also need to be hard wearing and resistant to both water and chemicals. Where appropriate they should be sloped for drainage. Suitable materials include – non-slip ceramic or quarry tiles, epoxy resin or vinyl sheet.

Ceilings

These may be solid or suspended, but must be made from materials that are smooth, impervious, non-flaking, easy to clean, light coloured, not easily damaged by condensation and capable of supporting ventilation grilles and pipe work. Ideally they should be coved at the junction to walls to aid cleaning.

Condensation and flaking paint are both potential contamination risks with ceilings. This can be reduced by using emulsion paints that are slightly absorbent but at the same time are capable of being cleaned.

Suitable surfaces include plasterboard with taped joints, skimmed plaster and corrugated sheeting provided that they are all treated so they may be cleaned easily.

If there are suspended ceilings, the space above them must be accessible for routine inspection.

Walls

Walls must be smooth, impervious, non-flaking, light-coloured and capable of being thoroughly cleansed. The surface should resist spills, chemicals, grease, heat and impact. Pipe work that passes through walls must be adequately sealed and any brackets must be easy to clean. Ideally, they should be coved at the junctions with floors and ceilings to aid effective cleaning.

Suitable surfaces include glazed tiles, plastic sheeting with stainless steel sheeting in heavy use areas and as splash backs behind sinks and worktops.

Windows

Windows should be constructed to prevent the accumulation of dirt and internal window ledges sloped so that they cannot be used as shelves. Windows opening to the outside should be fitted with insect-proof screens that can be easily removed for cleaning. Any windows without insect screens, opening to the outside, should be fixed so that they cannot be opened during production.

Doors

Doors should have smooth, non-absorbent surfaces that should be easy to clean and, where necessary, disinfect. Internal doors in areas where food is prepared should be fitted with self-closing doors. Doors opening to the outside should be tight fitting and pest proof.

Services

Gas

It is important that pipe work is installed to allow access for cleaning. Flexible connections are recommended so that it is easy to clean around the supply pipes without the risk of damage.

Electricity

There should be an adequate number of power points – controls should be fixed clear of equipment to prevent them becoming dirty or wet during cleaning, electrical wiring should be protected by waterproof conduit, isolators and all switches should be flush fitted.

Water

There must be a good supply of potable water ideally direct from a mains supply.

Floor surfaces should be easy to clean

Walls should be smooth, impervious and light coloured

Windows should be fitted with insect screens

Drainage

Drainage facilities must be adequate for the purpose intended and designed and constructed to avoid any risk of contamination. It should be laid with an adequate fall and flow from clean (high risk) to dirty (raw). All gulleys must have traps and internal inspection holes should be double sealed. Grease traps may be necessary.

Ventilation

There must be suitable and sufficient means of natural or mechanical ventilation and it should flow from clean to dirty areas. It must prevent excessive heat, condensation, dust and steam and remove odours and contaminated air. When planning a ventilation system, expert advice should be sought to ensure that food rooms will have the recommended number of air changes. Good ventilation provides reasonable working conditions, reduces humidity and temperatures, which encourage bacterial multiplication, and helps to reduce grease and the staining of ceilings, so reducing the need for frequent redecoration. It is also important that extraction systems are designed and installed to allow for effective routine cleaning.

Lighting

There must be suitable and sufficient lighting to help staff to maintain a clean, safe working environment without eye strain. Fluorescent tubes should be fitted with diffusers to prevent glare and to contain the glass and prevent contamination if there is a breakage.

Work surfaces

Any work surface in areas where food is handled and, in particular, those in contact with food must be smooth, impervious, free from cracks that could harbour dirt or food scraps and easy to clean and, where necessary, disinfect. Ideally they should be made of stainless steel, which in addition to the above is also resistant to corrosion and non-toxic.

Facilities for hand washing

Adequate and suitably located facilities must be provided for hand washing. These might be located at the entry to a food preparation area to encourage staff to wash their hands every time they enter, or in the sales area of a delicatessen counter so that hands can be washed at any time without having to leave the area.

These facilities must be used for hand washing only and provide hot and cold water (or a mixture of the two), ideally by means of foot, knee or elbow operated taps to reduce the risk of cross-contamination from hands. Suitable materials should also be provided for cleaning hands (for example, a liquid bactericidal soap and possibly a nail brush that is changed and/or disinfected on a regular basis) and for the hygienic drying of hands (preferably single-use, disposable paper towels).

Toilet facilities

An adequate number of toilets must be provided that are suitably ventilated, either naturally or mechanically, and do not lead directly into areas where food is handled. If they are not in a totally separate area, as a minimum requirement, there must be a separate, ventilated area between the toilet and the food preparation area. Hand washing facilities must also be provided, and ideally, as described above, with taps that involve no hand contact.

Changing facilities

Adequate changing facilities for staff must be provided – normally in the form of a locker for outside clothing and footwear – and ideally separated from the food preparation area.

Facilities for cleaning and disinfection

Adequate facilities must be provided for the cleaning, disinfecting and storage of cleaning equipment. These facilities may range from an area with a double sink to areas containing large-scale machinery for the cleaning and disinfecting of equipment and machine parts. These facilities should be constructed of corrosion resistant materials (usually stainless steel), be easy to clean, and have an adequate supply of hot and cold water.

Provision must also be made for the storage of cleaning agents and disinfectants, which must not be stored in areas where food is handled.

Food premises must have adequate and suitable handwashing and toilet facilities

Facilities for washing food

In the majority of food businesses the facilities for washing food should be separate to those for washing food equipment and utensils. The size, or type, of the food business might dictate that both operations be carried out in the same sink. However, this would only be permitted if there was no risk to food safety.

The design of equipment

All surfaces in contact with food should be inert and non-toxic. Nothing from the material used must be able to migrate into, or be absorbed by, the food. Food-contact surfaces should be smooth, impervious and non-porous so that particles of food, bacteria or insect eggs are not caught in microscopic cracks.

Equipment should be designed to:

- avoid crevices and spaces where particles could collect inside or on outer surfaces
- avoid offering pest harbourage inside
- allow all surfaces in contact with food to be properly cleaned and, if necessary, disinfected
- protect the contents from external contamination, such as objects falling into the equipment
- resist, as necessary, heat, acid and corrosion
- be durable
- prevent the risk of food being contaminated by substances, such as rust.

Installation and siting of equipment

All equipment should be installed in a way that allows staff to clean the surrounding area thoroughly. Ideally, equipment should be mobile – racks, refrigerators, ovens and other equipment can be mounted on castors, with brakes on all wheels. Immobile equipment should have a space of at least 25cm between the floor and its underside to allow for cleaning underneath. Alternatively, the base should be sealed to the floor. To make cleaning easier, immobile and fixed equipment should be positioned in island sites – in the middle of a room – with moveable equipment against walls.

Gas and electricity supply pipes should be flexible and it should be possible to isolate or disconnect them. Motors and switches should be waterproof and there should be enough electrical sockets installed to avoid trailing wires and cables. It should be possible to clean all guards.

Any equipment positioned directly above open food should be free from rust, flaking paintwork, condensation and mould.

Waste control

How waste is managed and controlled both inside and outside food premises is discussed in Chapter 13.

Legal considerations

Regulation (EC) No. 852/2004 on the hygiene of foodstuffs requires food premises to meet certain standards – for instance, the premises must be kept clean and maintained in good repair and condition. The following summary of the regulation also acts as a resume of the key points of design and construction covered in this chapter.

The regulations state that the layout, design and construction of premises must:

- allow for adequate cleaning
- protect food from cross-contamination
- protect against the accumulation of dirt and contact with toxic materials
- protect against condensation, mould and the shedding of particles into food.

In addition, there must be adequate:

- supplies of potable water
- sanitary facilities – lavatories must not lead directly into food rooms
- storage for food at suitable temperatures
- drainage, lighting and ventilation
- hand washing facilities and separate provision for washing food
- changing facilities for staff, where necessary.

The layout, design and construction of premises must allow for adequate cleaning and protect food from contamination

In rooms where foodstuffs are processed, treated or prepared the regulations lay down additional requirements, including the following:

■ Floor surfaces and walls must be maintained in sound condition and be easy to clean and disinfect.

■ Materials should be impervious, washable and non-toxic. Floors may need to allow adequate surface drainage, while walls need to be smooth to an appropriate height.

■ Ceilings must be designed, constructed and finished to prevent the accumulation of dirt, reduce condensation and mould growth and prevent the shedding of particles.

■ Windows and other openings must be constructed to prevent the accumulation of dirt and, where necessary, be fixed closed during food production. In some cases, fly screens may be appropriate.

■ Doors should be easy to clean and made of smooth, non-absorbent material.

■ Surfaces, including equipment surfaces, must be maintained in sound condition, be easy to clean and, where necessary, disinfect. They should be of smooth, non-toxic, washable materials.

■ There must be adequate facilities to wash and disinfect work tools and equipment.

Moveable and/or temporary premises, including market stalls, marquees, domestic premises used for the preparation of food for sale, and vending machines must be positioned, designed and constructed so that they can be kept clean and maintained in good repair and condition to avoid the risk of food contamination and harbourage of pests. Where necessary, personal hygiene equipment and food washing facilities must be provided. (For further details see page 152.)

Equipment, articles and fittings that come into contact with food must be kept in good condition, be made of suitable materials and be kept clean and, if necessary, disinfected to minimise any risk of contamination. They must be installed in a way that allows for adequate cleaning of the surrounding area. (Also see page 152.)

Examples of supervisory management

Any changes to either buildings or equipment may require the implementation of new procedures or the modification of existing ones as part of the food safety management system. Supervisors have a role in:

■ helping to set standards and create procedures, such as cleaning procedures and schedules, maintenance standards, equipment condition standards and design briefs for new building work

■ communicating standards and procedures to staff

■ training staff to clean and maintain equipment and the building and to report any damage

■ taking appropriate cleaning and pest control measures.

■ ensuring the provision of resources such as time, materials, cleaning equipment, maintenance budgets, servicing and 24-hour call-out contracts for equipment and pest control

■ monitoring a range of records and practices, such as checklists for the condition of premises, equipment checklists for the cleaning and swabbing of surfaces and records for pest contractors' work and equipment faults

■ motivating staff – through a variety of approaches such as refresher training

■ taking any necessary corrective action – staff meetings, check lists, posters and disciplinary action – to maintain standards

■ checking (auditing) and reviewing the system.

Chapter 13
Cleaning, disinfection and the disposal of waste

Cleaning can be defined as the application of energy to remove dirt, grease and other soiling. Disinfection is the reduction of micro-organisms to a level that is regarded as safe. A clean environment, or one that is free from dirt and contamination, is essential to food safety as well as being a legal requirement for food businesses.

Potential hazards

- **Bacterial contamination** – when cleaning is inadequate, or when contaminated cleaning cloths are used.
- **Cross-contamination** – when the same cleaning equipment is used in:
  - areas designated for the storage or preparation of raw foods as well as in areas set aside for high-risk foods
  - dirty areas as well as clean areas
  - washrooms as well as food preparation areas.
- **Physical contamination** – from inadequate waste disposal or from inadequate cleaning of equipment and surfaces, which may leave grease, burnt food and other food debris that could contaminate the next batch of food to be prepared.
- **Chemical contamination** – from incorrect use of chemicals, inadequate rinsing, inappropriate use of chemicals that are not safe for food areas, unsuitable storage of cleaning chemicals close to food or decanting and storage of chemicals in food containers.
- **Pest infestation** – as a result of inadequate cleaning and waste disposal.

The need to clean

It is a legal requirement to keep premises, equipment, utensils and materials clean to help to ensure the safety of food. Effective cleaning can also have an important impact upon a business's reputation and profitability.

The benefits of cleanliness

Cleanliness brings many benefits including:

- reducing the risk of food-borne illness or food spoilage
- removing materials and food that could provide harbourage and nourishment for pests
- helping the prompt identification of a pest infestation
- preventing the physical contamination of food
- ensuring that the working environment is pleasant, safe and attractive – which, in turn, promotes economical and effective working methods
- reducing the risk of accidents to staff, customers and others affected by the work operation
- promoting a favourable image to customers.

Consequences of poor standards of cleanliness

If cleaning is not carried out or is ineffective, it can result in an increased risk of:

- food-borne illness and food spoilage
- prosecution – the business will not be compliant with the law
- pests – dirty and untidy premises attract pests and infestations will be more difficult to identify
- physical contamination – from a number of sources
- an unpleasant, unsafe and unattractive working environment – which, in turn, results in wasteful and unproductive working methods
- high staff turnover as good staff are unlikely to stay
- loss of business and profitability because of the unfavourable image presented to customers.

Cleaning equipment

They are many types of cleaning equipment and cleaning systems including:

- sinks and tanks
- cloths, brushes, mops and buckets (colour coding of such equipment is widely used to identify clearly which equipment should be used in certain areas – for example, sanitary areas and for high- and low-risk storage, production or preparation areas – thereby reducing the risk of cross-contamination)
- mechcanical aids, such as vacuum cleaners, dishwashers and low-pressure jet washers that may be used in combination with foam for cleaning walls and other surfaces in high-risk areas
- clean in place (CIP) systems for certain types of equipment – such as beer lines in a pub or pipe work and tanks in a dairy – where it is not practicable to break equipment down for cleaning and disinfection.

Cleaning equipment should be fit for purpose

Cleaning

The process of cleaning involves the removal of soil, food residue, dirt, grease and other objectionable matter and is achieved by using energy in various ways. It may involve physical or kinetic energy such as wiping, brushing or scrubbing or, mechanical energy provided by machines such as a floor polisher or a dishwasher. Most cleaning operations also use thermal energy provided by hot water or steam, often in conjunction with chemical energy in the form of detergents, disinfectants or sanitisers.

Detergents are chemicals, or a mixture of chemicals, that help to remove grease and food particles so that surfaces are prepared for the action of disinfectants. The removal of grease and food particles may remove some microbes, but many will survive. Cleaning must be followed by disinfection if potentially harmful bacteria are to be reduced to acceptable levels.

Disinfection

The process of disinfection involves the reduction of pathogenic bacteria (but not spores or toxins) to levels that are neither harmful to human health nor to the quality of food. Disinfection may be carried out using:

- chemicals, either separately or in combination (disinfectants)
- heat, preferably moist heat, at temperatures above 82°C
- steam.

Sanitisers

These are chemicals combining both a detergent and a disinfectant. If used correctly, sanitisers can both clean and disinfect. They are only usually effective in situations where soiling is light; if soiling is heavy the disinfectant action may not be sufficient to reduce bacterial loads to acceptable levels.

What to disinfect

All areas that need to be disinfected in a food operation should be clearly identified on the cleaning schedule (see page 98). Any surfaces coming into direct contact with raw or high-risk foods must be cleaned and disinfected after every use. The same will apply to items that are frequently handled such as knives, containers or other utensils. Hand-contact surfaces, such as handles and taps, also need to be cleaned and disinfected on a regular basis. The use of a bactericidal liquid soap for hand washing in food premises is essential.

The frequency of both cleaning and disinfection of non-food contact surfaces such as floors and walls may be reduced and, in many situations, cleaning only may be sufficient.

Food-contact surfaces:

- food preparation surfaces, such as chopping boards
- knives, small utensils, dishes, containers
- food machinery ranging from parts of a production line or a conveyor to mixing bowls, slicers, mincers.

Hand-contact surfaces:

- handles on doors, cupboards, drawers, ovens, refrigerators, freezers
- taps
- light switches, controls, levers
- clothes, brushes, mops used for cleaning
- lids to waste bins
- telephones
- toilet seats, flush handles, door handles
- nail brushes.

Food-contact and hand-contact surfaces must be disinfected regularly

When using disinfectant always follow the manufacturer's instructions

Guidelines for disinfection

Disinfection needs to be carried out carefully to ensure that is successful and safe.

- Ensure that chemicals used in food areas are food-safe.
- Read and make sure that you understand the manufacturer's instructions before using a disinfectant.
- Always follow the manufacturer's instructions.
- Make up the solution to its specified strength, using measured amounts of chemicals and water.
- Never mix different chemicals.
- Ensure thorough cleaning of all surfaces prior to disinfection
- Rinse away all traces of detergent from clean surfaces before attempting to disinfect them – otherwise the disinfectant will not be able to work properly.
- Use a fresh solution of disinfectant every time you carry out a cleaning task and do not be tempted to top up an existing solution.
- Do not soak mops or cloths in disinfectant solutions for long periods, such as overnight, because the solution weakens and may allow bacteria to grow.
- Always leave disinfectants on a surface for the contact time recommended by the manufacturer.
- Rinse thoroughly, unless the manufacturer's instructions state that rinsing is unnecessary.

Cleaning and disinfection – a six-stage process

The process of cleaning and disinfection can be broken down into the following six stages:

1. **Pre-clean** – removal of loose dirt and soiling by wiping, scraping, rinsing or soaking.
2. **Main clean** – loosening the remaining dirt and soiling by the use of detergents.
3. **Intermediate rinse** – removal of dirt and soiling and chemicals.
4. **Disinfection** – reduction of the remaining bacteria to a safe level.
5. **Final rinse** – removal of the disinfectant.
6. **Drying** – air drying or with paper towels.

Cleaning (the first three stages) alone will suffice if disinfection is not necessary – for example when cleaning a floor surface. Disinfection must always be preceded by the cleaning stages if it is to be effective and reduce micro-organisms to a level that is safe. Disinfection (chemical or hot water) will be inhibited if soiling and grease are present. If sanitisers are used, stages 2–4 can be combined.

The following examples illustrate how the stages identified above may be followed and modified, depending on the location and the task involved.

A heavily soiled work surface in a high-risk food preparation area

The cleaning and disinfection of a heavily soiled work surface in a high-risk food preparation area could be carried out using the following method, based on the six stages identified above:

- remove as much loose soil from the work surface as possible before
- clean with a solution of detergent in hot water at approximately 50°C to break down and loosen all remaining grease and soil
- rinse with warm water to remove all the loosened soil and detergent from the surface, thus preparing the surface for disinfection (it is also important to ensure that in addition to removing the soil, all residues of detergent are also removed as they can both reduce the effectiveness of a disinfectant)
- disinfect with a chemical disinfectant, prepared to the manufacturer's directions and leave for the recommended 'contact time' (the time required for a disinfectant to reduce pathogenic and spoilage micro-organisms to a level that is safe for human health)
- rinse with warm water to remove all traces of disinfectant
- if required for immediate use, wipe dry with a disposable cloth, otherwise allow to air dry.

As an alternative to using a chemical disinfectant, hot water – at a temperature of 82°C or above – may be used after rinsing off all the loosened soil and detergent. Using hot water will also speed up air drying and, therefore, drying with a disposable cloth may not be necessary.

A work surface that is not in a high-risk food area or one that is lightly soiled

If the work surface is not in a high-risk food area, or the surface is only lightly soiled, using a sanitiser may be a more appropriate alternative. As a sanitiser is a chemical combination containing both detergent and disinfectant two stages are effectively removed, as follows:

- removal of excess soil
- wash down with a solution of sanitiser as directed by the manufacturer to break down and loosen all remaining soil and grease, and to disinfect
- rinse with warm water to remove all traces of sanitiser
- if required for immediate use, wipe dry with a disposable cloth, otherwise allow to air dry.

Some sanitisers – also known as anti-bacterial surface cleaners – do not have to be rinsed off after use and are safe to use on surfaces where food is prepared. They are often used in dining areas where the table is sprayed with a sanitising solution that is then wiped off with a cloth in preparation for the next customer.

Crockery, cutlery, glasses, utensils, chopping boards or removable parts of machinery

In situations where high-risk food-contact surfaces are involved – as discussed above – the full six stages with either a chemical disinfectant or hot water over 82°C should be used. This would also apply to situations where crockery, cutlery, glasses, utensils, chopping boards or removable parts of machinery are washed by hand in a double sink (for example, as found in small catering, retail or manufacturing situations where there are no automatic dishwashing facilities). Hot water over 82°C, rather than a chemical disinfectant, is usually used in the second sink to disinfect. As mentioned earlier, using hot water over 82°C will aid rapid air drying, especially with crockery, cutlery and glasses, thus removing the need for drying by hand and the additional risk of cross-contamination.

Dishwashing machines

Dishwashing machines, which may be used for crockery, cutlery, glasses, utensils, chopping boards or removable parts of machinery, follow similar principles to those already discussed. A typical process involves:

- removal of excess food and careful loading, usually into removable racks, into the machine
- a detergent wash at approximately 55–60°C
- rinse cycle with water over 82°C and rinse aid to disinfect
- air dry in machine or remove racks to drain and air dry.

Cleaning and disinfecting other equipment

The cleaning and disinfection of other machinery or equipment – for example, fixed machines or pipe-work (such as found in clean in place CIP systems in dairies and breweries), production lines, conveyors or equipment such as scales or slicing machines that cannot be washed in a sink or a dishwashing machine without causing damage – will follow similar principles to those already described. However, because they are all individual pieces of equipment or machinery, how this is to be carried out will need to be described individually as part of a cleaning schedule.

Cleaning schedules

Effective cleaning and disinfection is a vital component of food safety in any food operation and the use of a cleaning schedule is a way of ensuring that this takes place. Cleaning schedules involve a documented plan of cleaning and disinfection routines for all parts of a food operation and are based on answering the following four basic questions:

What needs to be cleaned?

Everything that needs to be cleaned must be listed on the cleaning schedule – from food preparation surfaces and equipment to floors and walls. It is important that all parts of the food operation are covered.

How will cleaning be carried out?

To include a description of the cleaning method, the chemicals and equipment (for example, disposable cloth, nylon brush, floor scrubbing machine, etc.) that should be used, any safety precautions that need to be taken and any protective clothing or equipment that need to be worn. It should also include an indication of the time required to carry out the task.

When will it need to be cleaned?

This shows how frequently cleaning tasks should be carried out – for example, chopping boards to be cleaned and disinfected after every use, floor to be cleaned at the end of every shift and disinfected weekly.

Who will do the cleaning?

Depending on the task, this could be a designated person, everyone working in a specific part of the operation or an outside contractor.

It is important that monitoring takes place to ensure that the cleaning schedule has been followed and that it meets the specification. Whoever, carries out the cleaning should sign the cleaning schedule to confirm that the work has been done and it should be countersigned, by a supervisor or manager, to confirm that it has been checked and it meets the specified standard. Additional checks may also involve taking surface swabs or using rapid microbiological checks.

The control and disposal of waste

From a legal point of view Regulation (EC) No. 852/2004 on the hygiene of foodstuffs is quite specific about food waste stating that it must:

- be removed from areas where food is handled as quickly as possible and should not be allowed to accumulate
- be deposited in closable containers that are easy to clean and disinfect
- be stored in areas that can be kept clean and, where necessary, free from animals and pests
- not constitute a direct or indirect source of contamination.

If waste is not effectively controlled, both inside and outside food premises, it can be a source of bacterial and physical contamination and can also attract pests.

Internal waste

When considering how waste control fits into the general design of food premises, any waste that is collected internally must not be allowed to come into direct contact with food products. Ideally routes for taking waste out of food premises should not cross routes taken by food products within.

Internal containers for food waste should have tight fitting lids, be lined with disposable polythene sacks and, ideally, be foot-operated to avoid any hand contact. These containers generally need to be situated close to working areas. However, they must be positioned where there is no risk of them coming into direct contact with food. In some situations waste containers are in constant use and are un-lidded. This is acceptable as long as they are emptied on a regular basis. Internal waste containers must never be allowed to overflow and should always be emptied at the end of a work period or at the end of the day, otherwise they will attract pests. Unless containers are disposable they must be easy to clean and disinfect on a regular basis. It is also good practice for disposable polythene waste sacks to be distinct from other similar bags.

Food waste should not be allowed to accumulate

Keep waste in suitable containers

Once food waste has been removed from a food preparation area it should be placed into lidded or sealed containers to await disposal. At this stage it may be either stored inside or outside the premises. If it is stored inside, it must be in an area away from any food preparation areas and be easy to clean and disinfect. In some situations waste has to be stored under refrigeration prior to collection for disposal (for example with meat or fish waste) – again, this waste needs to be stored away from food preparation areas and in a unit that is easy to clean and disinfect.

Refuse such as cardboard, clean packaging materials and paper does not necessarily have to be stored in closed containers. However, it must be stored so that it is not a contamination risk to food.

To reduce the risk of being used in error, any food items that have been rejected, recalled to a supplier, or are not for sale – although not technically waste – must be clearly identified and stored in a designated area.

External waste

Food waste stored outside awaiting collection must be kept separate from any contact with incoming or outgoing food in an area that is easy to keep clean. Depending on the size of the operation, this area may need a supply of hot and cold water, a suitable surface (for example, concrete) that is impervious and easy to clean and effective drainage. All containers – these may range from bins to large skips or compactors – must have tight-fitting lids or covers so that pests are unable to gain access. The containers must be easy to clean and disinfect. Regular collection of waste is vital – if it is allowed to accumulate, it may start to smell or overflow and attract pests.

Many large retail outlets provide facilities for the public to recycle paper, cardboard, bottles and cans. Recycling facilities should be sited away from any entrances or open windows of the store and must be kept clean, have suitable containers that are emptied on a regular basis.

All waste containers must have tight-fitting lids

Regular collection of waste is vital

Legal considerations

To satisfy the requirements of Regulation (EC) No. 852/2004 on the hygiene of foodstuffs:

- food premises must be kept clean and maintained in good repair and condition
- equipment must be effectively cleaned and, if necessary, disinfected
- food waste must not be allowed to accumulate in food areas.

Examples of supervisory management

Supervisors have an important role to play in the area of cleaning and disinfection by:

- setting a good example
- helping to set standards, such as visual and bacteriological standards, and creating procedures, such as cleaning schedules
- communicating required standards and procedures to staff
- training staff in the use of cleaning chemicals and equipment, methods of cleaning and practices
- ensuring the provision of resources such as materials, equipment and time
- implementing the safe use of chemicals and cleaning equipment
- monitoring a range of records and practices, such as ensuring that chemicals are in the right place and that replacement equipment, including cleaning cloths, is available
- motivating staff to maintain standards, using a variety of approaches such as refresher training, staff meetings, checklists, posters and, if necessary, disciplinary action
- auditing, including activities such as the signing off of cleaning tasks, reviewing the system or the bacteriological swabbing of hands
- taking any necessary corrective action.

Chapter 14
Pest control

Food pests cause thousands of pounds' damage every year to food premises and business reputations, while infestations are a major reason for enforcement action and prosecution. However, every food organisation can take steps to prevent an infestation. Methods of control include environmental, physical and chemical measures.

Potential hazards

- **Bacterial contamination** – from bacteria on pests and excreted by them onto food.
- **Cross-contamination** – from bacteria left by pests on food-contact surfaces.
- **Physical contamination** – from pests' bodies, eggs, hair, droppings, etc.
- **Chemical contamination** – from careless use of insecticides and rodenticides, or from residual insecticides.

Common pests

A food pest is any living creature capable of contaminating food. Common pests in food businesses include:

- rodents – rats and mice
- birds – pigeons, sparrows, starlings, gulls
- insects – flies, cockroaches, ants, wasps, stored product insects.

Food pests must be controlled because:

- it is a legal requirement
- they carry disease
- they cause food wastage
- they damage buildings and fittings
- they cause customer complaints.

It is a legal requirement to control pests

Food pests carry disease and cause food wastage

Infestation

If you discover a pest infestation, you must take immediate action to deal with it. The steps you take will depend upon your job responsibilities and training, but may include:

- closing the premises
- finding the cause of the infestation and ensuring that it will not recur
- ensuring that contaminated food is removed and destroyed
- arranging for the premises to be cleaned thoroughly
- ensuring that food is removed before chemical sprays are used
- checking that surfaces and equipment are cleaned after treatment and before being re-used so food does not become tainted
- organising the treatment and any necessary repeated treatment of the premises by competent pest control operatives
- inspecting the premises for maintenance defects and ensuring that effective repairs are carried out promptly
- liaison with an Environmental Health Practitioner (EHP) and/or a pest control contractor.

The food business operator must ensure that any contracted pest control companies are competent and provide reports of any surveys and action taken. A written record should be made about each visit and should be kept by the food business. Using contractors does not remove or reduce a company's legal responsibility if pests contaminate food.

Methods of pest control

Pests may be controlled by a variety of methods:

- environmental
- physical
- chemical.

Environmental methods are usually used to **prevent** pest infestation, while physical and chemical methods are usually used to **control** infestations.

Environmental control – prevention

The key points involve:

- the design, maintenance and proofing of the premises
- good housekeeping
- the denial of food, moisture and harbourage
- the correct storage of food and packaging.

Pests need food, water, shelter and security to thrive. If these are denied, pests will not survive. Good housekeeping is essential. A pest may occasionally gain access to even a well-proofed building, but if the premises are kept clean and tidy, large numbers of pests will not be able to breed. Pay special attention to staff changing rooms, locker rooms, dining areas, lift shafts, food stores and waste areas. All spills of food and liquid should be cleared up immediately. Waste should be removed and disposed of in a hygienic manner – bins must have well fitting lids and be of an adequate size. Removing sources of water – such as dripping taps, leaking roofs and damaged gutters – will aid control. Denial of access includes ensuring that:

- doors are well fitting and are kept closed unless in use
- windows have insect screens and air bricks have a wire mesh behind them
- the building is well maintained so that no holes are left, for instance, around pipes
- false ceilings, ducting and boxed-in pipe work have internal access points
- cavities in internal walls have been avoided
- cupboards, equipment and preparation tables can be moved for cleaning and inspection.

Guidelines for the prevention of pest infestation

- Remove unused equipment, vegetation and other harbourage areas from the site.
- Move and regularly check unused equipment and packaging.
- Keep all food in rodent proof containers and always replace lids.
- Check all raw materials – including packaging, equipment and food – on arrival and before they are stored.
- Ensure that outside areas are tidy and not overgrown with vegetation.

Eradication methods

If pests gain access to food premises, they must be destroyed by **physical** or **chemical** methods. When physical methods are used, the pest is caught and removed so the risk of food contamination is eliminated. However, if the infestation is large, physical control may be too slow and ineffective, so chemical methods are used. When chemicals are used, the pests do not die immediately and they may contaminate food if precautions are not taken. The use of chemicals must be carefully controlled to prevent chemical contamination of food.

Physical control

Methods include:

- traps
- sticky boards
- tracking powder
- electrocuting fly killers
- sticky flypapers
- thick inert gels – to deal with birds
- sprung wire systems – to deal with birds
- bird-scaring devices
- shooting
- mist netting.

Chemical control

Methods used include:

- rodenticides – either acute (when a single bait is used, for instance, in sewers) or chronic (multiple baits used in food premises over a period of time)

- insecticides – some sprays may be used for cockroach control, providing that all food is protected from contamination (although dichlorvos strips are unsafe for use in food areas, some residual insecticides may be suitable)

- narcotising drugs – for birds.

Common food pests

Rodents

Rats and mice should be controlled because of:

- the spread of disease, caused by:

  - food poisoning bacteria – such as *Salmonella*, carried on and/or in the bodies of rodents

  - contamination by rodent urine and droppings, which can lead to Weil's disease (leptospirosis) and other illnesses

  - parasites – including the cysts of *Trichinella spiralis*, a worm that lives in rats' intestines, which particularly affects raw pork and may survive when the meat is not cooked thoroughly

  - rat bites

- the possibility of wasting food, as a result of:

  - infestation of food and packaging materials, leading to loss of production, recall of contaminated foods, repackaging and the destruction of large quantities of food

- damage (leading to fires, floods or subsidence) to structures and service installations, such as underground water pipes and electricity cables, caused when rodents gnaw to wear down their incisor teeth

- likely financial loss, caused by any or all of the above

- legal requirements.

Physical control

A tracking powder, such as flour or talcum powder, is used to detect rodents by tail and foot prints. Traps are used to catch the survivors of chemical treatment or where there is a particular risk of food contamination by chemical methods. Traps may be laid with or without bait and must be examined daily. The advantage of trapping is that the rodent's body can be removed easily and disposed of safely – the animal cannot hide, die, decompose and smell somewhere, such as under the floor of a food room. Sticky boards are a piece of board covered with glue to which an animal sticks. They can be used to deal with the survivors of chemical treatment. They must be checked daily.

Chemical control

Rodenticides, which may be extruded from a gun as a paste, are often mixed with bait, such as cereal, fruit, fish or meat. The reaction to the chemical is either acute – and the animal dies after one feed – or chronic – so that the animal has to eat the bait for some time. Some rodents develop a resistance to certain chemicals, so the bait must be changed. Contact dust, such as bromadiolone, is also used. Animals pick up the dust on their feet and fur. It is then passed through the skin or is ingested as the pest cleans itself. Contact dust must not be used in food rooms or where food or equipment could be contaminated.

Characteristics and habitats of rodents

Brown rat (Rattus norvegicus)

Characteristics	20 to 25 cm / 200 to 500g / broad body / blunt nose / small ears / tail shorter than rat's body / variable colour, typically brownish with grey underside / large feet / omnivorous: prefers cereals, meat, eggs, fruit – needs access to water supply
Habitat	burrows in soil (especially underneath or close to buildings) sewers, food stores, rubbish dumps

Black rat (Rattus rattus)

Characteristics	18cm / 100 to 300g / slender body / pointed nose / large ears / tail longer than rat's body / variable colour, typically black or brown with grey-white underside / large feet / omnivorous: not as dependant on water as Brown rat
Habitat	will inhabit drier areas, climbs to upper stories of buildings, roof spaces, generally confined to port areas, grain stores

House mouse (Mus musculus)

Characteristics	8cm / 15 to 20g / small body, slender / slightly pointed nose / large ears / tail much longer than head and body / grey back, light grey belly / small feet / omnivorous: can survive with little moisture, generally getting sufficient from moisture in food
Habitat	buildings – generally lives close to food supply

Brown rat

Black rat

House mouse

Pigeon

Sparrow

Birds

The Wildlife and Countryside Act 1981 protects all wild birds, their eggs and nests except for certain species defined as pests – including feral and wood pigeons, house sparrows, starlings, some gulls, jackdaws, magpies and rooks.

Reasons for controlling pest birds include preventing:

- the contamination of food or equipment by droppings, feathers and nesting materials, which carry insects and mites
- the transmission of food poisoning micro-organisms, such as *Salmonella*
- blocked gutters, which may result in flooding and expensive repairs and maintenance
- the defacement of buildings – bird droppings contain an acid that attacks stone and paint
- the build up of droppings, which can result in offensive smells
- roosting on fire escapes and similar structures, causing a safety hazard
- non-compliance with legal requirements.

Environmental control

All possible points of entry need to be proofed to prevent the entry of birds. This may range from blocking small holes or gaps at roof level to the use of netting to cover larger potential access areas. Thick inert gels, sprung wires and spikes discourage birds from perching and roosting on buildings by making them feel insecure. Bird scaring devices include loud bangs, flashing lights and distress calls – but birds tend to ignore them after a while.

Physical control

Baited traps with non-return doors may be used for pigeons. Air rifles may be used, but food must be protected from metal pellet contamination. Mist netting may be fixed in the flight paths of birds: trapped protected species are released and pest species are killed by humane methods. This can only be carried out under licence.

Chemical control

Bait containing a narcotising chemical is used to sedate birds. Protected birds are then released and pest species are killed by humane methods. This technique is also strictly controlled and requires a licence.

Discourage birds from perching or roosting

Insects

Insects – including flies, cockroaches, ants, stored product pests (for example – flour beetles, grain weevils, flour moths and psocids or book lice) – need to be controlled because:

- many insects carry food poisoning bacteria
- they can contaminate food by their bodies, droppings, webs and eggs
- they can attack and destroy large quantities of food
- it is a legal requirement.

Flying insects – housefly, bluebottle and fruit fly
Flies infect food by:

- regurgitating partly digested food and enzymes as they eat
- continually defecating
- carrying bacteria, such as *Salmonella*
- physically contaminating food with their bodies, eggs, etc.

Life cycle of a fly

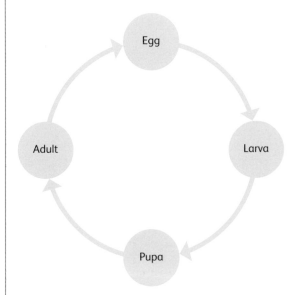

The speed of development varies with temperature – it may be less than three weeks from egg to egg.

Housefly

Oriental
cockroach

German
cockroach

Cockroaches

Cockroaches can carry various pathogens including *Staphylococci* and *Salmonella*. They may also contaminate food with their dead bodies, faecal pellets and moult debris (to grow into adults cockroaches shed their exoskeletons, or hard body coat, several times).

Oriental cockroach (Blatta orientalis)

Characteristics	24mm long / shiny dark red to black / omnivorous – will eat a wide range of food / nocturnal / can climb rough vertical surfaces / most common type
Habitat	congregates around water, cellars, kitchens drains, bakeries, refuse tips

German cockroach (Blatta germanicus)

Characteristics	15mm long / yellowish brown / omnivorous – will eat wide range of food – also attack packaging and textiles / nocturnal / can climb smooth vertical surfaces
Habitat	prefers constant, warm, moist conditions e.g. kitchens, laundries, restaurants

Ants

Ants (such as the black garden ant – *Lasius niger*) usually nest outside buildings, finding their way into food premises through small gaps and crevices and are generally treated as a nuisance. The exception is the Pharaoh's ant (*Monomorium pharaonis*) that nests indoors where there are warm conditions and relatively high humidity – for example, in hospitals, residential homes and bakeries. They are attracted to a variety of foods including meat, fat, bread and pastry. Pharaoh's ants can be come contaminated by pathogens from drains and other sources such as clinical waste – it is, therefore, vital that nests are detected and eradicated.

Stored product insects

There is a large group of stored product pests that attack a wide range of foods including: grains, cereals, flour, biscuits, dried fruits, spices and nuts. They include beetles (flour and biscuit beetles), moths (flour and warehouse moths), weevils (grain and rice weevils), lice (book lice or psocids that also infest packaging materials) and mites.

Physical control of insects

Sticky boards may be used to check for insect infestation. Sticky fly paper, without chemicals, can be used in areas where the public are not admitted. Electrocuting fly killers (insectocutors) may be used to kill flying insects, which are attracted to a charged grid by ultraviolet light. Care must be taken when positioning insectocutors so that dead flies cannot fall or be blown into food – for example, not above work surfaces. They are most effective when placed away from windows and fluorescent light and properly maintained. Insectocutors should not be used where there are high concentrations of flour, sugar, or dust because of the risk of explosion.

Pharoah's ant

Rice weevil

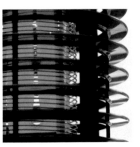

Electrocuting fly killers (insectocutors) may be used to kill flying insects

Chemical control of insects

Insecticides may be used as a spray or contact dust, or in a gel or be included in bait. Thermal vaporisers, dichlorvos strips or residual insecticides must not be used in food rooms because the substances they emit may contaminate food, as may the dead insects. Residual insecticides may be used in food areas if all food and equipment is removed or covered. However, thorough cleaning must take place before the area is used for food again.

Fumigation may be necessary if stored product insects are found. Insecticidal lacquer bands may be used on walls and around doors. Insect growth regulators and pheromones to attract insects may be used for long-term control.

Integrated pest management

Rather than tackling pest problems as and when they occur, many food businesses work closely with pest control contractors actively to prevent infestation. This approach, known as 'integrated pest management' focuses on preventative measures rather than simply the use of physical and chemical pest control measures when an infestation occurs. Supervisors have a key role to play in ensuring that it is effective. In particular by:

- escorting pest control contractors when they initially survey premises
- accompanying pest control contractors during their inspection visits or when they have been called out to follow up on an infestation
- monitoring pest control contractor visit reports and following up recommendations
- ensuring that all deliveries into the premises are inspected for pests
- carrying out inspections on physical and environmental controls such as fly screens or insectocutors
- training staff to identify and report signs of pest infestation
- ensuring staff follow standards set for stock control, cleaning, good housekeeping, waste control, building repair and maintenance, and that checklists in these areas are maintained.

Legal considerations

- Regulation (EC) No. 852/2004 on the hygiene of foodstuffs requires food to be placed and/or protected against contamination and that food premises be designed, constructed and maintained in good repair and condition to prevent contamination by pests. In addition, the regulation states that windows and other openings may require insect screens and refuse stores must be designed to prevent pest access.

- Regulations also state that it is an offence to sell unfit or contaminated food – and pests compromise food safety. Food premises with a serious pest infestation may be shut down under closure procedures.

- The Prevention of Damage by Pests Act 1949 requires occupiers/owners of land (except for farmland) to advise the local authority of any rodent infestation. The Act also requires local authorities to take steps to ensure that the area under their control is kept free from rodents.

- Under the Health and Safety at Work etc. Act 1974 employers must ensure, as far as reasonably practicable, the health, safety and welfare of employees – and pests may affect their working conditions.

Examples of supervisory management

Supervisors have an important role to play in preventing pest infestation including:

- setting a good example
- helping to set standards for stock control, cleaning, good housekeeping, waste control, building repair and maintenance and creating procedures for preventing and eliminating infestation
- monitoring the work of pest contractors and surveys of the premises
- communicating standards and procedures to staff
- creating and maintaining checklists for maintenance, cleaning schedules, stock delivery/rotation and surveys of the premises, signs of pests, reporting procedures, good housekeeping, stock control, cleaning, and waste control
- training staff to identify and report signs of pest infestation and to use good housekeeping and pest prevention methods and stock rotation
- ensuring the provision of resources such as cleaning and proofing materials and checklists
- supervising pest control contracts, the regular inspections for signs of pests, the checking of deliveries and physical and environmental controls, such as fly screens and insectocutors
- monitoring a range of records and practices, such as contractor's pest book, surveys for infestation
- using a variety of approaches, such as refresher training, staff meetings, check lists, posters and even disciplinary action, to motivate staff to maintain standards
- checking (auditing) and reviewing the system
- taking any necessary corrective action.

Part 3: Food safety management systems

Chapter 15
Hazard Analysis and Critical Control Point (HACCP)

Hazard Analysis and Critical Control Point (HACCP) is a formal system of hazard analysis that has international recognition as a cost-effective way to control food-borne illness.

Background to HACCP

Codex was established in the 1960s by the Food and Agriculture Organization and the World Health Organization of the United Nations. It is a global organisation and has three principal aims:

1. To protect the health of consumers.
2. To ensure fair practices in international food trade.
3. To issue guidance and codes of practice, aimed at promoting the harmonisation of all food standards.

The HACCP system originated in the 1960s as part of a collaboration between the US National Aeronautics and Space Administration (NASA) and the Pillsbury Company aimed at providing safe food for astronauts on space missions. At that time food safety was generally measured by the number of complaints or the incidence of food-borne illness and the quality of the finished product was often determined by end testing. Food safety assessments tended to concentrate on how clean premises were and what the structural condition of the building was like. Although these all contribute towards food safety, what happens while food is being produced – food handling, processing and storage practices in particular – are usually the most significant factors in whether or not a food is going to be safe to eat.

HACCP moved the emphasis away from end testing to identifying hazards as they occur during all stages of production and looking to either eliminating them or, if this is not possible, by controlling them at critical points in the production process. By following this approach the final product should be safe and end testing becomes largely unnecessary.

Following several serious outbreaks of food-borne illness in the 1970s and 1980s both in the US and elsewhere the use of HACCP systems expanded and started to become a legal requirement, particularly in parts of the food manufacturing sector.

In 1997 the Codex Alimentarius Commission issued a set of guidelines aimed at standardising and improving the application of HACCP. The guidelines are based on seven principles that are set within a series of twelve steps (*see* page 116) that need to be followed.

HACCP pre-requisites

HACCP is not a stand alone system. Procedures covering the general principles of hygiene need to be established and operational if the implementation of a HACCP system is to be effective. What is required will vary depending on the size and type of food business but generally procedures should be in place to cover the following areas.

Supplier specification

Raw materials and packaging should only be purchased from approved suppliers. This may involve written specifications and, where appropriate, supplier audits.

Design and structure of premises and equipment

There should be a clearly defined linear flow to the process from the delivery of raw materials through to the despatch or sale of the finished product without crossing over and the risk of cross-contamination.

A planned maintenance programme should be in place covering both the building and all equipment, including any internal water storage tanks or ventilation systems. Equipment, such as probe thermometers, ovens, weighing scales, laboratory testing equipment, should be regularly calibrated.

Personal hygiene

Management should provide appropriate protective clothing, hand washing facilities, toilets and changing facilities. Staff should be trained and there should be procedures in place covering for example – the wearing of protective clothing, permitted jewellery, smoking and eating on the premises, reporting illness, using waterproof dressing to cover cuts.

Cleaning, disinfection and the control of waste

This should be a documented system using cleaning schedules. Provision must be made for the effective control and removal of waste.

Pest control

This may involve having a contract with a recognised pest controller, ideally as part of an integrated pest management system.

Storage and stock control

Raw materials and finished products need to be stored in the correct conditions – for example, at the correct temperature, off the floor and secure from infestation by pests. Procedures should be in place for the rotation of stock to ensure that it does not exceed its use-by date and that it is used in the correct order. Raw materials and finished product should all be traceable and there should be procedures for the secure holding ('quarantine') and effective removal of sub-standard or rejected material.

Training

Food handlers need to be fully trained for the job they carry out. In addition to the comments above on the need for personal hygiene training they may also need additional training in any of the other areas noted above as well as any specific training related to their own particular job.

Food handlers must be trained

The 12 steps of HACCP

1. Assemble HACCP team

2. Describe product

3. Identify intended use

4. Construct flow diagram

5. On-site confirmation of flow diagram

6. Conduct a hazard analysis and consider control measures

7. Determine the Critical Control Points

8. Establish critical limits for each CCP

9. Establish a monitoring procedure for each CCP

10. Establish corrective actions

11. Establish verification procedures

12. Establish documentation and record keeping

Steps 6–12 are also defined as the seven principles of HACCP.

Implementation of HACCP – 12 steps

With the pre-requisites satisfied, HACCP can be implemented.

Step 1 Assemble the HACCP team

Ideally this should be a multidisciplinary team using individuals with product knowledge as well as individuals who may have specialist technical knowledge or managerial skills. The number of people involved will, of course, depend on the size of the business but it is unlikely that one person will have all the required knowledge. In a large business, the HACCP team is likely to be large and will include representatives from different levels and different departments. For example, it may include technical managers, production managers, company engineers, microbiologist, quality assurance (QA) staff, specialist hygiene staff, line managers and supervisors and individual representatives with particular specialist knowledge (for example, operatives on particular production or packing lines). In a small operation it might just include the food business operator and whoever can help without disrupting day-to-day activity. In this situation an external consultant may be used.

The team should be aware of the hazards involved in the business and also how they are controlled. Also, a general knowledge of what is involved in setting up a HACCP system is desirable and, therefore, it may be appropriate for some or all of the team members to receive some formal training before starting the implementation process. At least one team member should have detailed knowledge of the complete implementation procedure.

Step 2 Describe the product

In a manufacturing situation a full description of each product needs to be drawn up, including information on:

- ingredients and formulation
- raw material suppliers
- storage conditions
- processing conditions
- packaging
- shelf life
- distribution methods
- microbiological data
- physical/chemical parameters (e.g. pH, a_w)

In catering or retailing situations, where there are multiple products, it may be appropriate to group products with similar characteristics or processing steps in order develop the HACCP plan (for example – keeping a range of meat pies hot prior to sale in a retail outlet or holding ready-to-eat, high-risk salads in a chiller unit prior to service in a restaurant).

Step 3 Identify intended use

Questions that need to be answered might include:

- Will the product be consumed by any vulnerable groups? (For example, elderly people, young children, pregnant women, people who are ill in hospital or individuals who suffer from allergic reactions.)
- What is its shelf life?
- Will it need to be refrigerated, frozen or can it be stored at ambient temperatures?
- Are there any special requirements? (For example refrigerate after opening and use within three days, remove foil before micro-waving, if frozen after purchase fully defrost before cooking.)

Butcher selling raw meat only

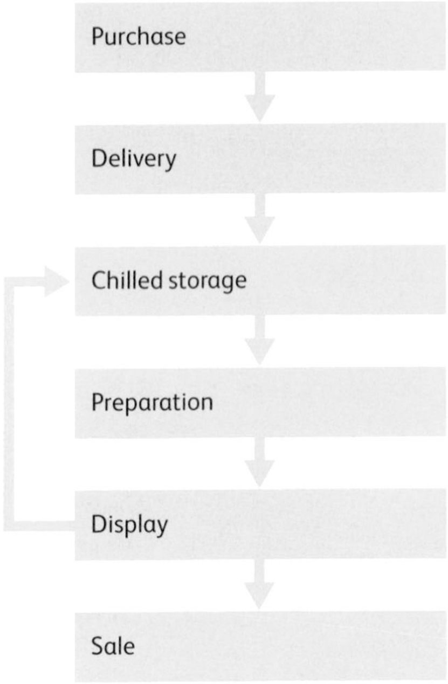

Purchase

↓

Delivery

↓

Chilled storage

↓

Preparation

↓

Display

↓

Sale

Cooked roast chicken

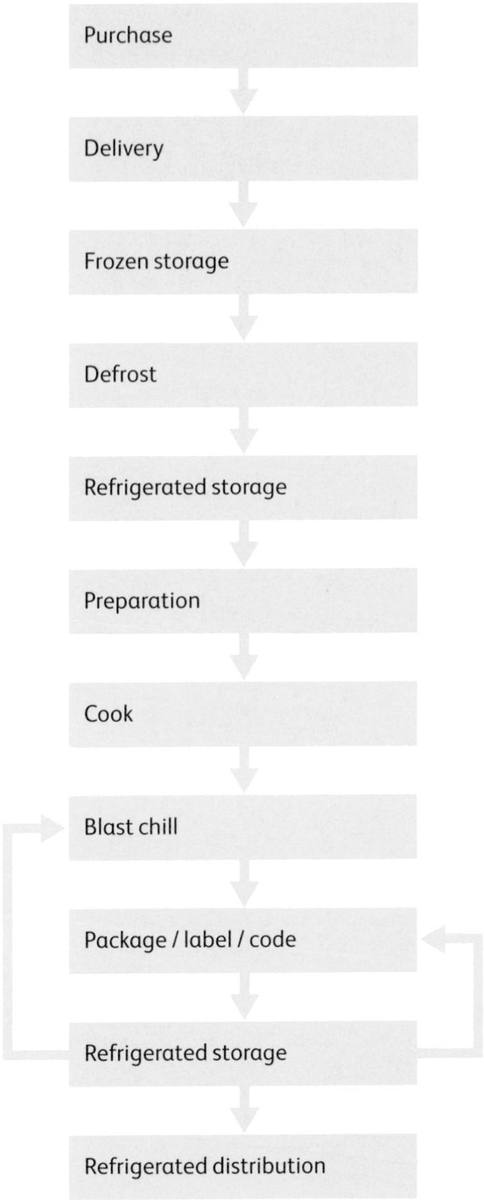

Purchase

↓

Delivery

↓

Frozen storage

↓

Defrost

↓

Refrigerated storage

↓

Preparation

↓

Cook

↓

Blast chill

↓

Package / label / code

↓

Refrigerated storage

↓

Refrigerated distribution

Ready-to-eat breaded meat pieces

Oil purchase	Breadcrumb purchase	Water	Batter mix purchase	Meat pieces purchase
Receipt and storage	Receipt and dry storage		Receipt and dry storage	Receipt and chill storage
	Sieve		Sieve	
			Mix with water	Coat with batter
				Coat with breadcrumbs
				Check weight
	Balance tank and filter			Deep fry
				Cool
	Packaging			Label
				Storage
				Distribution
				Consumer

Step 4 Construct a flow diagram

The flow diagram, to be drawn up by the HACCP team, should cover all the steps or stages in the operation for a specific product. This may be a relatively simple flow diagram – as illustrated by the example of a butcher selling raw meat only (see page118) or the business that cooks and sells cooked roast chicken (see page118). The flow diagram for ready-to-eat breaded meat pieces (see page119) is more complex and it contains several ingredients. The flow diagram usually covers every stage in a process from the purchase of raw materials through to the point of sale or distribution of the finished product to the final consumer.

Step 5 On-site confirmation of flow diagram

It is important to confirm that what happens at all stages, and at all times of processing, actually matches what has been identified and included on the flow diagram. For example, different food handlers may have different ways of carrying out a particular operation – tasks may be carried out differently on different shifts, different ingredients may be being used or there may be seasonal variations or food handlers may take short cuts. Therefore, the flow diagram should be checked against actual practice several times during the working day and ideally by as many different members of the HACCP team as possible. Any differences not identified at this stage can potentially affect the final outcome and reliability of the hazard analysis.

Step 6 Conduct a hazard analysis and consider control measures

This is the most complex stage of the process. Having collected all the preliminary information on the product this step requires that the HACCP team to:

- identify all the hazards that may occur at each stage in the process from primary production through to the point of consumption
- decide which hazards need to be either eliminated or reduced to acceptable levels, if safe food is to be produced
- consider how likely each hazard is to occur in the process and how severe the health effects are likely to be
- assess the likelihood of either the survival or the multiplication of any microbiological hazards

- assess the possible production or persistence in the food of toxins, chemical or physical hazards
- decide what control measures can be applied for each hazard.

Having considered these points the HACCP team should now be in a position to agree all the significant hazards that need to be eliminated or reduced to acceptable levels to make the food product safe.

In the context of food safety a **hazard** is any biological, physical, or chemical agent or condition with the potential to cause harm to the consumer. Hazards are usually identified as:

- microbial
- physical
- chemical
- allergenic.

For more information on hazards see Part 1 and in particular Chapters 2, 4, 5 and 6.

A **control measure** is any action taken to prevent or eliminate a food safety hazard or reduce it to an acceptable level – for example, high-risk foods are generally stored under refrigeration to control the multiplication of bacteria, food is cooked to eliminate or destroy pathogens, flour is sieved to prevent physical contamination.

Part 2 provides more detailed information on measures that may be taken to control hazards – in particular see Chapter 8.

Step 7 Determine critical control points

A **critical control point** (CCP) is a step or point in the process where a control can be applied. It is essential to either eliminate or reduce the hazard to an acceptable level. If a hazard is not controlled, it could make the final product unsafe and, as a result, possibly cause harm to the consumer. Identification of the CCPs enables management to concentrate resources at these points

In the case of the flow diagram for cooked roast chicken (see page 118) several opportunities can be identified where pathogenic bacteria – such a Salmonella species or Campylobacter species – could survive and multiply if they were not controlled. In particular at the following stages:

- delivery – initial high bacterial load on delivery from supplier

- frozen storage – poor temperature control (for example, a faulty freezer)

- defrost – inappropriate method used (for example, defrosted overnight at ambient temperatures)

- refrigerated storage – poor temperature control (for example, overloaded refrigerator)

- preparation – held for a long time at ambient temperatures before prepared for cooking

- cooking – insufficient to achieve required core temperature.

Controls should be in place at all the above stages. However, there is only one stage of the six identified above where the hazard, if it is not controlled, could result in high levels of pathogenic bacteria in the final product. There may have been inadequate controls prior to delivery, in frozen storage, on defrosting, in refrigerated storage awaiting preparation, and in the preparation of the chickens, but as long as they are thoroughly cooked pathogens would be destroyed. Cooking is the only one of these six steps that is critical and for this reason it is the only one that is a critical control point.

In the case of the butcher selling raw meat only (see page 118) there are controls that need to be in place to limit the multiplication of pathogenic bacteria at all stages of the business from delivery through to the point of sale. However, from a microbiological point of view, none of these stages are critical control points. As he only sells raw meat, the final control – ensuring that the meat is thoroughly cooked and therefore safe to eat – is the responsibility of the consumer.

The flow diagram for ready-to-eat breaded meat pieces (see page 119) has three stages for controlling potential physical contamination – the sieving of the batter mix prior to mixing with water, filtering of the oil in the balance tank prior to frying and the sieving of the breadcrumbs prior to coating the ready-to-eat meat pieces. In all three cases, they are the only points in the process where possible physical contamination from these three raw materials can be controlled. Therefore, they are all critical control points.

Step 8 Establish critical limits for each CCP

A critical limit is a criterion that separates acceptability from unacceptability. Therefore, levels need to be established to ensure that wherever a control measure has been set for a critical control point it is sufficient to eliminate, prevent or reduce the hazard to an acceptable level.

For the business producing cooked roast chicken 80°C held for at least six seconds is a safe core temperature. This would be the minimum temperature you would want to accept when setting a critical limit. To allow for small adjustments to be made in a process while still staying within acceptable limits, and to avoid having to reject food if the minimum temperature is not met in some of the samples you check, it is usual to set a higher temperature as the target to aim for. In this case it might be decided to set a target temperature at 85°C held for at least six seconds with a tolerance of +/- 5°C. Therefore any temperatures between 80°C and 90°C would be acceptable, but 85°C would be the ideal, or target, temperature. To provide an example – a core temperature of 81°C would still be acceptable and within the critical limit range of 80–90°C but, to be safe and to achieve the target of 85°C, you would need to make a small adjustment to the oven temperature.

Critical limits for sieve and filter sizes in the production of ready-to-eat breaded meat pieces will depend on the minimum acceptable aperture size that could be used to sieve the batter mix and the breadcrumbs or to filter the oil. Once these sizes have been determined, a fixed critical limit could be set for each sieve or filter (setting targets would not be appropriate).

Step 9 Establish a monitoring system for each CCP

Monitoring involves making observations or taking measurements to assess whether a critical control point (CCP) is under control. Having set a critical limit for a particular CCP, it is necessary to check that it is being met. This is not just an individual check – CCPs need to be monitored at all times and they must be able to detect loss of control. Checks should ideally provide information in time to make any necessary adjustments and, therefore, to prevent a critical limit being broken or violated. If monitoring is not continuous, there must be sufficient checks to guarantee that a CCP is in control.

Product – Ready-to-eat breaded meat pieces				
Process Step	Sieving of breadcrumb	Sieving of batter mix	Filter on oil balance tank	Check-weigher (prior to deep frying)	Deep frying
Hazard	Physical contamination from breadcrumb and packaging	Physical contamination from batter mix and packaging	Physical contamination from oil and container	Microbiological Survival of *Salmonella* / *E. coli* species/ *Campylobacter* species if breaded meat pieces above specified weight.	Microbiological Survival of *Salmonella* / *E. coli* species / *Campylobacter* species
Control Measure	Nylon mesh sieve	Nylon mesh sieve	Stainless steel filter.	Check-weighing of all breaded meat pieces.	Thorough deep frying
CCP	Yes	Yes	Yes	Yes	Yes
Critical Limit	Retain all physical contamination unable to pass through 2500 micron (2.5mm) vibrating sieve. Tolerance – none	Retain all physical contamination unable to pass through 1000 micron (1.0mm) vibrating sieve. Tolerance – none	Retain all physical contamination unable to pass through a solid stainless steel filter with 750 micron (0.75mm) diameter holes. Tolerance – none	110g – 130g Target 120g Tolerance +/- 10g	Instant 86°C – 94°C Target 90°C Tolerance +/- 4°C
Monitoring Procedures	Sieve integrity visually inspected continuously when in use. Tailings inspected continuously when in use and retained for Quality Assurance inspection	Sieve integrity visually inspected continuously when in use. Tailings inspected continuously when in use and retained for Quality Assurance inspection	Filter visually inspected before every drum of oil emptied into balance tank. Any physical contaminants retained for Quality Assurance inspection	All breaded meat pieces passed through automatic check-weigher prior to deep frying and any overweight pieces rejected. Check-weigher and reject function checked at start up, every 10 minutes, and end of production run, with calibrated check weights	Check core temperatures of three random ready-to-eat breaded meat pieces, at start up, every 10 minutes, and end of production run, with disinfected temperature probe
Corrective Actions	Stop process and replace sieve if damaged. Empty and clean breadcrumb holding hopper and re-sieve all contents before continuing process. Stop process if excessive / unacceptable physical contamination retained on sieve. Advise supplier if physical contamination excessive / unacceptable. Inform manager. Consider new supplier of breadcrumb	Stop process and replace sieve if damaged. Empty and clean batter mix holding hopper and re-sieve all contents before continuing process. Stop process if excessive / unacceptable physical contamination retained on sieve. Advise supplier if physical contamination excessive / unacceptable. Inform manager Consider new supplier of batter mix	Stop process and replace filter if damaged. Empty balance tank and re-filter oil before continuing process. Stop process if excessive / unacceptable physical contamination retained on filter. Advise supplier if physical contamination unacceptable. Inform manager. Consider new oil supplier	In case of check-weigher breakdown or malfunction stop production and investigate cause of problem. Identify and hold all deep fried breaded meat pieces back to last check on check-weigher with calibrated weights. Carry out any necessary repairs. Contact supplier if weight control of individual meat pieces unacceptable. Inform manager Consider new supplier of meat pieces	Stop production and investigate cause of problem. Identify and hold all ready-to-eat breaded meat pieces produced since the last temperature check. Adjust time/temperature settings. Deep fry for longer. Carry out any repairs if necessary. Inform manager
Records	Record details of all corrective actions taken including any contact with supplier	Record details of all corrective actions taken including any contact with supplier	Record details of all corrective actions taken including any contact with supplier	Record details of all corrective actions taken	Record all temperatures taken. Record details of all corrective actions taken

Product – Cooked roast chicken	
Process Step	Cooking
Hazard	Microbiological
Control Measure	Survival of *Salmonella* / *Campylobacter* species
CCP	Thorough cooking
Critical Limit	Yes
Monitoring Procedures	80°C – 90°C for 6 seconds Target 85°C
Corrective Actions	Tolerance +/- 5°C
Records	For each batch check core temperature of a chicken from top, middle and bottom of oven with a disinfected probe.

Most monitoring will involve checks that can be carried out quickly – the checks usually relate to on-line processes and lengthy analytical testing would not be appropriate. For this reason a physical measurement, such as checking the core temperature of a cooked product or food in a refrigerator using a probe thermometer, is preferred to microbiological testing as it can be done rapidly and often indicates the microbiological control of the product.

In the case of the business producing cooked roast chicken, assuming that chickens are cooked in bulk, the most appropriate method of monitoring, to ensure that all chickens reach an acceptable core temperature on cooking, would be by using a temperature probe. Initially it may have been necessary to the check the core temperatures of every chicken. Experience may have indicated that this was not necessary and that monitoring chickens from the top, middle and bottom of the oven for each batch was sufficient to guarantee control of the CCP. Assuming this approach was adopted, a further important consideration would be the weights of individual chickens – it would almost certainly not be possible to guarantee control of the CCP if the weights were variable. They would, therefore, need to be purchased to a specified weight and this would also need to be monitored.

Following on from above, the flow diagram for ready-to-eat breaded meat pieces includes check-weighing of individual breaded meat pieces before deep frying. Assuming this is a continuous process, the breaded meat pieces will pass along the deep fryer on a conveyor for a specified time in order to reach a safe core temperature. This can only be achieved if individual breaded meat pieces conform to a specified weight range. To avoid the possible undercooking of overweight pieces or the overcooking of those that are underweight, continuous weight monitoring of all breaded meat pieces is necessary to guarantee control at this point – overweight or underweight pieces would need to be rejected. This is a CCP as it is the final stage in the process where, if not controlled, pathogenic bacteria could possibly survive and therefore still be present in the final ready-to-eat product.

Monitoring the integrity of the two sieves and the filter in the ready-to-eat breaded meat pieces process would be by visual inspection. The sieves for the breadcrumb and the batter mix could most likely be visually checked whenever they are in use. It may be sufficient to check the filter for the cooking oil at the start and end of the day.

All monitoring checks of CCPs need to documented and should be signed by the person(s) doing the monitoring and countersigned, usually by their supervisor or manager.

Step 10 Establish corrective actions

Specific corrective actions must be developed for each CCP in the HACCP system so that any deviations can be dealt with whenever they occur. If a critical limit is breached, the safety of the final product cannot be guaranteed – corrective action has to be taken to bring the situation back into control.

How this is going to be achieved should be fully documented for each CCP so that, whenever a CCP is not met, there is no doubt as to what action should be taken. In this situation there are two main aims:

- to make the product safe
- to prevent a recurrence of the problem

If cooked roast chickens are not reaching the target temperature when cooked it may be possible to bring the process back into control by cooking them for longer and checking again. To prevent it from happening again it may also be decided to increase the oven temperature. Both these solutions may not be possible if there is a fault with the oven. If an alternative oven cannot be used, production will have to stop and product that has not reached the target temperature will have to be rejected.

If the oil filter on the ready-to-eat breaded meat pieces line is found to be damaged and the monitoring procedure only states that it be visually inspected on a weekly basis, apart from having to stop production and reject product, it may be necessary to recall product. Traceability procedures should be in place to cover this scenario. In addition, to avoid having to recall any product in the future, it may be decided that monitoring procedures be changed to an hourly visual inspection.

For all the above situations it is vital that documented procedures are in place so that the correct decisions are made. Also, deviations must be documented as part of HACCP record keeping.

Step 11 Establish verification procedures

Verification involves being able to confirm that the HACCP system is working correctly by applying methods, tests or other evaluations that are in addition to the monitoring procedures already in place. This may involve auditing the HACCP system to ensure that the hazards identified are correct and that they are being controlled, especially at CCPs, to ensure food safety. Other methods may include random sampling, organoleptic evaluation, microbiological testing or analysing raw materials, work in progress and finished product.

Verification should be carried out by someone other than the person who is normally responsible for monitoring and corrective actions. Verification activities may be carried out by external consultants, experts or by qualified third parties. Internal audits should be carried out by suitably-qualified individuals from other departments and, depending on their specific responsibilities, this may be part of a supervisors' role.

An internal audit to verify that a HACCP system is working effectively may include:

- a review of the HACCP system and plan – this should include details of everything involved in setting up the HAACP system from a record of the HACCP team, a description of the product and its intended use, the flow diagram, identification of hazards, determination of control measures, CCPs, critical limits, monitoring procedures, corrective actions, verification procedures and review documentation
- a review of documentation and records (as summarised in Step 12 (see page 125)
- a review of any deviations – including details of actions taken, such as products rejected or recalled, records of food-borne illness, customer complaints
- confirmation that CCPs are under control.

The frequency of verification needs to be sufficient to confirm that the HACCP system is working effectively. In situations where there are no apparent changes, it may be acceptable to agree to review the HACCP system on a six-monthly or annual basis to confirm that the scientific, legal or best practice basis of the HACCP system. If there has been an outbreak of food-borne illness attributed to the business or a series of similar complaints, HACCP systems need to be urgently reviewed. They should also be reviewed if there have been any changes in the following:

- **raw materials** – for example, a new supplier, substituting frozen vegetables for fresh when out of season

- **recipe or formulation** – for example, removal of artificial flavouring, reduction in seasoning levels

- **processing methods** – for example, reduced cooking time, modified mixing method

- **equipment** – for example, purchase of a larger oven, new refrigeration unit

- **packaging** – for example, changes to the barrier film to extend shelf-life

- **method of distribution** – for example, product to be held in new distribution centre, lowered product distribution temperature

- **organisational changes** – for example, staffing levels, hours of working, management reorganisation.

Step 12 Establish documentation and record keeping

Both documentation and record keeping are essential requirements of any HACCP system. The amount of information retained will vary with the size and type of the business, but it should be sufficient to verify that HACCP controls are in place and that they are being maintained. Also, if required, documentation and records, will help to support a due diligence defence in court.

Examples of documentation and record keeping might include:

- Detail of the hazard analysis – for example, product description, flow diagram, information on hazards identified, critical control points and the determination of critical limits, minutes of HACCP team meetings.

- Records of all monitoring activities and corrective actions where appropriate – for example, checking refrigerator and freezer operating temperatures, cooking temperatures, cooling times, delivery checks.

- Records of all other general procedures relating to hygiene that are in place – for example, raw material supplier lists and specifications, cleaning schedules, pest control records, stock control data, training records.

- Records of any changes that have been made – for example, as a result of the purchase of new equipment, changes in the recipe or formulation, review following an increase in customer complaints.

Chapter 16
Food safety management in catering and retail

To help small catering businesses and small retail businesses comply with requirement for a documented food safety management system based on Codex HACCP principles, the Food Standards Agency has developed a food safety management pack known as *Safer Food, Better Business*.

The *Safer Food, Better Business* packs, one for catering and one for retail, are based on a set of safe methods and a diary to help food business operators run their businesses effectively.

Safe methods

Each pack has a set of safe methods sheets highlighting safety points relating to a particular topic:

- cross-contamination
- cleaning
- chilling
- cooking
- management.

The first four topics are commonly referred to as the '4 Cs'.

Each safe method sheet:

- explains why the safety points are important
- asks the food business operator to identify how things are done in his/her business and what checks should be carried out to ensure they are effective
- advises what to do if things go wrong
- suggests how to prevent problems happening again.

Safer Food, Better Business – Safe methods

Cross-contamination	Personal hygiene Cloths Separating foods Pest control Maintenance Food allergies Physical and chemical contamination
Cleaning	Cleaning effectively Clear and clean as you go Your cleaning schedule
Chilling	Chilled storage and displaying chilled food Chilling down hot food Defrosting Freezing
Cooking	Cooking safely Foods that need extra care Reheating Checking your menu Hot holding Ready-to-eat-foods
Management	Opening and closing checks Extra checks Using a temperature probe to validate methods are safe Training and supervision Customers Suppliers and contractors Stock control

By working through each safe method sheet the food business operator can identify the specific parts of the pack that are relevant to the particular business and use this information to produce a specific food safety management system.

Safe methods – cross-contamination

So, for example, under cross-contamination the safe method sheet for cloths identifies that they are one of the main causes of cross-contamination in a kitchen. It recommends that single-use cloths be used wherever possible and that they are thrown away after each task to ensure that any bacteria picked up by the cloth are not spread.

Further safety points identify what should be done if re-useable cloths are used. In particular:

- they must be taken away for thorough washing after being used with raw meat, poultry, eggs or raw vegetables and any surfaces that have touched these foods

- make sure that they are thoroughly washed, disinfected and dried between tasks

- if they are washed in a washing machine, it should be on a hot cycle

- if they are washed and disinfected by hand, ensure that all food and dirt has been removed before disinfected in hot water.

The food business operator is asked to identify how he/she would clean re-usable cloths to ensure that they are safe, if they are still to be used in the business.

In addition there are suggestions on:

- the best type of cloth to use for different jobs – for example, disposable clothes for washing dishes or single-use paper towels for wiping surfaces or mopping up spills

- what to do if things go wrong – for example, if dirty cloths are being used in the kitchen – and how these situations can be prevented

- how to manage problems – for example, by considering where to store dirty re-usable cloths or where to keep new/clean cloths.

Cloths – a principal cause of cross-contamination

Disposable, single-use cloths are recommended

Safe methods – cooking

Cooking is generally a critical control point as, in a catering context, it is usually the last opportunity, prior to consumption, to ensure that any remaining bacteria are destroyed. In a conventional HACCP system this is usually achieved by extensive monitoring procedures involving documented temperature measurement. This is generally neither possible nor practical in most catering situations and, for this reason, simple visual checks are usually followed to ensure that the food is safe. This approach is followed in the safe methods for cooking.

For example:

- check birds (for example, roast chicken or turkey) are cooked properly in the thickest part of the leg – the meat should not be pink or red and the juices should not have any pink or red in them
- check processed meat products (for example, sausages or beefburgers) are hot all the way through with no pink or red in the centre
- check liquid dishes (for example, gravy or soup) bubble rapidly when stirred
- check combination dishes (for example, lasagne, fish pie) are hot (steaming) in the centre
- check prawns have changed colour and texture
- 'extra' checks might include probing with a sanitised digital thermometer probe.

Safe methods – management

The management category of *Safer Food, Better Business* is more specific in that it brings together the safe methods considered necessary to ensure food safety covered by the 4Cs in the first part of the pack.

It suggests that by carrying out opening and closing checks every time the business opens and closes, the basic standards necessary to make sure the business makes food safely should to be maintained. It identifies lists of opening and closing checks (as shown on page 130) and suggests appropriate additional checks.

It also suggests any extra checks, which may not have to be carried out on a daily basis, be identified:

- any maintenance work – for example, clearing drains, cleaning extractor fans
- pest control checks – for example, looking for signs of infestation
- calibrating equipment – for example, a temperature probe.

It describes safe methods for using a temperature probe to validate that cooking, hot holding, chilling and storage methods are safe.

Once safe methods have been decided it is essential that staff are trained and supervised in their use and a record of this should be kept in the daily diary.

There are also safe methods for using customer feedback as an indicator of how well the business is being managed, how to handle suppliers and contractors and effective stock control.

Opening checks – carried out at the start of the day

- fridges, chilled display equipment and freezers working properly

- other equipment (for example, the oven) working properly

- staff fit for work and wearing clean work clothes

- food preparation areas are clean (work surfaces, equipment, utensils, etc.)

- ample supplies of hand washing and cleaning materials (soap, paper towels, cloths, etc.)

Closing checks – carried out at end of the day

- no food left out

- food past its 'use by' date has been thrown away

- dirty cloths removed for cleaning and replaced with clean ones

- waste removed and new bags put in bins.

The diary

The law requires that food is safe to eat. It also requires that there is a written record of what the business does to protect food safety. Part of the written record can be a completed file of safe methods for *Safer Food, Better Business* as discussed so far, the remainder is contained in the diary.

The diary contains:

- week-to-view diary

- summary of opening and closing checks to be done every day

- 4-weekly review

- staff training record

- suppliers' list

- cleaning schedule

- 'prove it' records.

The week-to-view diary should be signed every day to confirm that:

- opening and closing checks have been completed

- agreed safe methods for the business have been followed.

If anything **different** happens, or something goes **wrong** the food business operator should make a note in the diary of what happened and what he/she did. The food business operator is not required to record every action taken, only those taken to make sure that food is safe to eat. This is known as 'exception reporting'.

The diary has a four-weekly review that allows food business operators to check that methods used in the business are up to date and that they are still being followed.

Part 4: Supervisory management

Chapter 17
The management process

All food businesses must be properly managed if they are to be successful. Supervisors play an essential part in management by influencing the behaviour of others and helping to turn the business's aims into everyday reality.

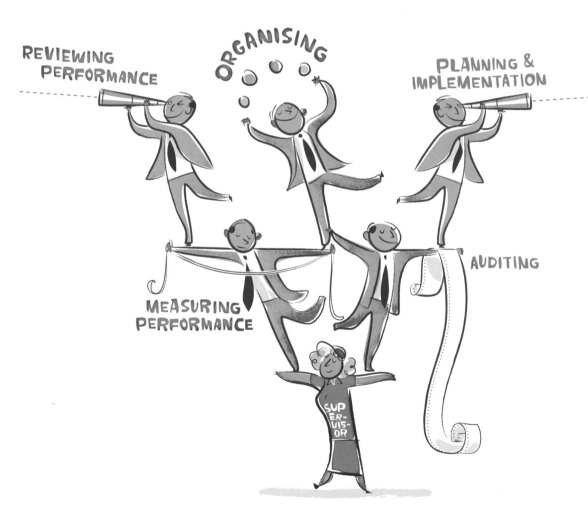

Management

The manager's role includes understanding the company's requirements, planning, organising, motivating staff and controlling processes, activities and standards. The supervisor's role is to assist in these activities.

The management process

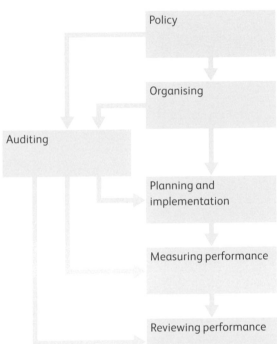

A supervisor will assist in many management tasks

Policy
This includes the general intentions, approaches and objectives of the business.

Organising
This involves designing and establishing responsibilities and relationships.

Planning
This involves working with management, deciding upon objectives, methods of implementation, priorities and the allocation of resources – people, money and time.

Measuring performance
The collection of information about the effectiveness of plans and standards may involve checking or monitoring. Monitoring may be active, such as checking the temperature of a refrigerator, or reactive, such as receiving a customer complaint.

Auditing
This is the structured process of collecting information about the efficiency, effectiveness and reliability of a system and drawing up plans for corrective action.

Reviewing
This involves making judgements about performance and decisions about improving it by using information from the measuring and auditing activities.

Chapter 18
The role of the supervisor

Supervisors' attitudes, enthusiasm and approach play a major part in helping to motivate staff to maintain acceptable standards and to follow agreed procedures, while supervisors' knowledge of the workplace and its systems and day-to-day problems help to influence future policy.

This chapter focuses on some of the main supervisory activities:

- monitoring and control methods
- food safety policy and its implementation
- quality assurance
- food safety training and the communication of policies to employees
- assisting in the investigation of an outbreak of food-borne illness.

Monitoring and control methods

Food safety cannot be left to chance. Standards for cleanliness, disinfection, maintenance, personal hygiene and pest control must be established. The quality of the raw ingredients and the finished product should be specified in visual, bacteriological or chemical standards. There should also be monitoring procedures to ensure that the specified standards are always achieved. It is the supervisor's role to communicate specifications and standards to employees – for example, by using schedules and charts, and by arranging staff training – and to ensure that they are maintained by using monitoring techniques. Such techniques may include:

- carrying out inspections and audits by spot checks, procedural checks or use of metal detectors
- completing checklists – for example, for cleaning, maintenance standards and waste food disposal
- checking that work has been completed – for example, cleaning or temperature recording.

Supervisors are also likely to be involved in the organoleptic assessment of food and bacteriological monitoring. Organoleptic assessment involves checking food by smell, taste, appearance, texture or even sound. Bacteriological monitoring can be for specific bacteria or for total viable counts (TVCs) of bacteria and may involve sampling raw materials, work-in-progress, finished products or random swabbing of surfaces and equipment.

Supervisors are likely to be involved in bacteriological monitoring

Food safety policy

The creation of a food safety policy helps a food business to set and implement standards in a planned and constructive manner. The policy should normally include:

- a general statement about the company's commitment to hygiene
- an organisational flow chart showing management responsibility
- rules for the standards set and the forms of monitoring and control used.

The policy, which may be expressed through a hygiene manual, may also include separate sections on all aspects of food safety including:

- personal hygiene
- pest control
- cleaning and disinfection
- preventing microbial, physical and chemical contamination
- staff training
- waste disposal
- temperature control
- premises and equipment
- monitoring and control procedures for suppliers and materials, from raw ingredients to finished goods
- quality assurance measures, including stock rotation
- procedures for dealing with visitors, contractors, suspected food poisoning, food complaints, product recall and enforcement action
- food safety management systems – such as HACCP.

Supervisors may not always play a direct part in shaping policy, but they have a crucial role in implementing and monitoring it.

Quality assurance

Quality **assurance** is an integrated management system for ensuring that product quality meets all the quality requirements all the time so that products are made correctly, without remedial work being necessary. Quality **control** is the process of measuring the actual quality of a product and comparing it against known specifications. Action should then be taken to eliminate any differences. An example of quality control is end-product testing. This can prove expensive and impractical. It encourages staff to believe that quality is someone else's job and, by the time a problem is discovered, remedial work or reworking may be impossible so that batches of food must be discarded.

The management team must develop systems to ensure that the food produced is of the right quality. Supervisors are usually expected to be involved in the development, implementation and continued use of such systems including the training of staff. There are internationally recognised standards for quality assurance systems, including ISO 9000 and EN 29000, but they are not suitable for every food business. Food businesses now have a legal responsibility to implement food safety management procedures based on the Codex principles of HACCP and quality assurance systems are generally compatible with this approach.

Quality assurance systems involve specifying, recording and monitoring tasks

Quality assurance systems involve:

- **specifying** what is to be done
- **documenting** how it is to be done
- **recording** what has been done
- **monitoring** what has happened and comparing it against the specification.

Various actions need to be taken to run a quality assurance system and supervisors may be involved in aspects of many of them:

- writing a quality system
- reviewing contracts with customers and their quality requirements
- documenting control systems and setting up procedures to ensure that documents are used correctly
- setting purchasing specifications
- establishing systems to check incoming material, including dealing with defective goods
- ensuring that all products are identifiable and traceable
- creating documentation systems for control processes
- establishing inspection and test procedures, including dealing with rejects from these procedures, and calibrating equipment such as metal detectors
- developing systems for non-conforming products
- ensuring that the systems include analysis of problems and corrective action
- creating documentation systems for food handling, storage, packaging and delivery
- keeping all quality assurance records (usually for at least the shelf life of the product)
- carrying out internal quality audits
- identifying training needs and keep records of the training received
- ensuring that statistical techniques are used for sampling.

Food safety auditing

In manufacturing and large retail food operations, supervisors are likely to be involved in auditing and inspection. The two terms are often used interchangeably, but each has a specific meaning.

Inspection involves ensuring that a raw material, finished product, process or food premises meets the required specification or standard and usually involves the collection of data by observation or discussion. Inspections may range from checking that raw materials on receipt conform to specification, to a detailed inspection that may be carried out by an environmental health practitioner in a food premises where there has been an outbreak of food-borne illness.

Auditing takes inspection a stage further and not only looks at whether or not standards or procedures are being met, but also at whether or not they are suitable to achieve stated objectives. Auditing is often used when verifying that a HACCP system is working correctly and is usually carried out by someone other than the person who is normally responsible for monitoring and corrective action. For this reason audits often involve external consultants, experts or qualified third parties.

An internal audit may be carried out by a suitably-qualified individual to verify the effectiveness of the traceability systems (*see* page 63) that are in place. This can be carried out, for example, by setting an 'audit trail' for a single raw material in a food product and following the documentation for its use from purchase through to the dispatch of the finished product.

Food hygiene training

Most food poisoning outbreaks are caused by the carelessness or lack of knowledge of the people involved in the food chain. A trained food handler understands why hygiene is necessary and ensures that good practice is followed. Supervisors have an important role to play in this area – as well as being actively involved in and possibly organising some training activities, they will generally witness first hand how effective it has been.

In addition to ensuring the production of safer food, effective staff training can contribute to profits by:

- safeguarding the quality of the product
- minimising food wastage
- reducing food complaints
- minimising the amount of supervision required
- giving staff increased job satisfaction, so reducing staff turnover
- increasing productivity.

Staff also gain from hygiene training, for example, by:

- improving their skills
- gaining greater confidence and working with less anxiety
- taking pride in their work.

The law (part of Annex II of Regulation (EC) No. 852/2004) requires food business operators to ensure that:

- food handlers are supervised and instructed and/or trained in food hygiene matters commensurate with their work activity
- those responsible for the development and maintenance of food safety management procedures based on HACCP principles have received adequate training in the application of the HACCP principles.

Training must be planned and regularly updated. It is essential that new staff receive essential food safety training as part of their induction before starting work. They may then receive informal, on-the-job training alongside experienced workers. This introductory training should be followed by a coherent training programme that is practical and relevant to the trainee and his or her work activities.

For staff not directly involved in the preparation or handling of high-risk, open (unwrapped) food such as waiters, warehouse personnel, or someone stocking shelves in a retail outlet appropriate further training may involve hygiene awareness instruction. This would cover for example – hygiene policy, personal health and hygiene, waste disposal, foreign body contamination, pest awareness and some hazard analysis information relevant to their particular job. The training would most likely be in-house and last from one to two hours.

Food handlers preparing and handling open, high-risk foods (for example, chefs, sales personnel on a delicatessen counter or food operatives on a production line producing ready meals) require more formal training. This may be a Level 2 course where food hygiene principles are considered in more detail. It may either be carried out in-house or by an accredited training organisation off-site and last approximately one day. On successful completion of the course and a short examination, candidates should receive a certificate.

Depending on their duties, supervisors or managers in food businesses may take either Level 3 (supervisory) or Level 4 (management) qualifications. Also, managers and supervisors need to take relevant HACCP training.

Refresher training, at an appropriate level, should also be provided at intervals for all staff.

A training record should show evidence of formal and informal training

Supervisors should assist investigations

Training records

Training records should be kept for all food handlers so that the company knows, and can provide evidence, that the staff have been properly trained. For example, this information may be required to demonstrate legal compliance and may also be used as part of a due diligence defence. A training record should show evidence of both informal and formal training – for example, on-the-job coaching as well as formal certificated and refresher training.

Assisting in the investigation of an outbreak of food-borne illness

Once a food premises has been identified as the possible source of an outbreak of food-borne illness an environmental health practitioner (EHP) will want to carry out a detailed inspection of the premises and investigate quality systems. Samples of suspect food or raw materials may be collected, possibly to be used as evidence if legal action is being considered. Equipment and work surfaces may be swabbed, photographs may be taken, staff may be interviewed. Relevant quality records, including records of staff sickness, will need to be available for inspection.

The EHP may request that all production be stopped or that no cleaning and disinfection be carried out until the investigation is complete. In extreme cases, premises may be closed down.

It may be necessary to recall any food that has already been sold and, therefore, sales records will need to be available as well as information on traceability or recall procedures.

As a supervisor, if an outbreak of food-borne illness is traced to your premises, you may be required to:

- notify the business operator
- tell any employee with a food-borne illness, or a suspected food-borne illness, to stay off work until he or she has seen a doctor and been cleared as safe to return to work with food
- leave the area un-cleaned until the EHP or the business operator is satisfied that it can be cleaned without interfering with the investigation
- remove from sale or delivery any food suspected of causing illness and, where appropriate, recall any food that has been sold or distributed

- keep samples of any suspected food and any unused food
- provide records and information – on issues such as personnel, sickness, food purchases and temperature control – for the EHP carrying out the investigation
- assist the investigating EHP – for example, by providing a room or other facilities or by making yourself or your staff available as required
- follow up any recommendations to prevent a recurrence of the problem.

Legislation

An introduction to food law

There are a large number of laws, regulations, codes of practices and guidelines covering the production, processing, distribution, retailing, packaging and labelling of foods in the United Kingdom.

The main purpose of this chapter is to consider the broad points of food law as it relates to most food businesses.

Types of legislation

New food hygiene legislation came into force in the UK in January 2006 affecting all food businesses – from primary producers to manufacturers, distributors, retailers and caterers. This legislation, as is now generally the case, originated from the European Parliament. Part of it was applied by national legislation – as with The Food Hygiene (England) Regulations 2006 (with equivalent regulations being applied for Wales, Scotland and Northern Ireland). A Regulation was applied directly and unchanged as an EU regulation, applicable to all member states – as with Regulation (EC) No. 852/2004 on the hygiene of foodstuffs. Both these regulations are considered in detail later in this section.

In addition there are local bye-laws – such as the prohibition of street trading in certain vicinities – which apply within a local authority's geographical area and have to be approved by a government minister before they can take effect.

There are also codes of practice, which are recommended standards. Although they do not have legal force, they can be used as guidelines by a court. One code of practice provides food safety enforcement officers with guidance on how to behave – for instance, during inspections – and how to enforce food safety laws. Certain sectors of the food industry, such as baking and catering, are covered by industry-specific codes of practice, called industry guides. They give advice on achieving appropriate standards of practice that comply with legislation. The industry guides are agreed by representatives of the specific industry and government, but have no legal standing (see also page 149).

Topics covered by legislation

Food safety legislation covers a wide range of subjects including:

- the production and sale of unfit, unsound or injurious food
- food contamination
- food importation
- the composition and labelling of food
- the control of food poisoning
- the registration of certain food premises and vehicles
- the hygiene of food premises, equipment and personnel
- the provision of sanitary accommodation, water supply and washing facilities
- hygiene practices, including temperature control and heat treatment
- health and safety at work.

Main legislation

All food businesses in the United Kingdom are covered by:

- The Food Hygiene (England) Regulations 2006 or equivalent legislation for Wales The Food Hygiene (Wales) Regulations 2006, Scotland The Food Hygiene (Scotland) Regulations 2006 and Northern Ireland The Food Hygiene Regulations (Northern Ireland) 2006
- Regulation (EC) No. 852/2004 on the hygiene of foodstuffs – a regulation detailing the general hygiene requirements for all food businesses and covering all member countries of the European Union.

There are two other regulations supplementing Regulation (EC) No. 852/2004:

- Regulation (EC) No. 853/2004 laying down specific hygiene rules for food of animal origin intended for human consumption
- Regulation (EC) No. 854/2004 laying down rules for official controls on products of animal origin intended for human consumption.

These regulations apply to businesses that produce animal-based foodstuffs, such as meat, poultry, seafood, milk and egg products, and then sell them to other businesses. Producers of animal-based foodstuffs generally need to meet additional requirements.

Many parts of The Food Safety Act, 1990 have been replaced by the Food Hygiene (England) Regulations 2006 or equivalent legislation for Wales, Scotland and Northern Ireland

Enforcing food safety legislation

Food safety legislation is enforced by 'authorised officers' (usually environmental health practitioners) who legally are described as individuals authorised in writing by an enforcement authority to act in matters arising under the regulations – that is, The Food Hygiene (England) Regulations 2006 and equivalent regulations for Wales, Scotland and Northern Ireland. Authorised officers' duties include:

- giving advice about food safety
- inspecting food premises
- investigating complaints about food including contamination and food poisoning
- examining food in food premises to decide whether it is fit or unfit for human consumption
- taking samples of food
- educating the owners, managers and employees of food businesses about food safety
- taking enforcement action including:
  - entering premises
  - serving notices – for example, hygiene improvement notice or a hygiene emergency prohibition notice
  - taking photographs and samples of food
  - seizing food and applying to a magistrate or sheriff to have unfit food destroyed
  - initiating criminal prosecution, including giving cautions and taking statements.

Food safety inspections

There are two main purposes for an inspection – to identify:

- the risks arising from the activities carried out and the effectiveness of the food business' own assessment and control of those risks
- any contraventions of food safety legislation, and to seek to have them corrected.

The inspecting officer must ensure that the food business operator is aware of the purpose of the inspection, which involves:

- an assessment of food safety hazards associated with the business
- a check on whether the business has a satisfactory system for assessing food hazards and controlling risks.

Officers discuss with the food business operator any necessary matters relating to hygiene systems and procedures. If there is not a satisfactory hazard system in place at the premises, the officer will carry out a more detailed visual inspection.

After the inspection, the officer should discuss the findings and provide a written report. Officers must always give clear guidance on the difference between advice they give and compulsory action required to comply with legislation.

Non-compliance with legislation

If a company or person does not comply with the appropriate legislation, legal action may be taken. This action may initially be informal advice, or a letter if the offence is not very serious and the officer feels that the company will put the matter right promptly. If more formal action is necessary, the inspecting officer may serve various notices or start prosecution proceedings or collect evidence.

If a food business fails to comply with a notice or a prosecution is started, then the business operator will face criminal proceedings.

In England and Wales food safety offences are heard in magistrates' or crown courts (depending on the seriousness of the alleged offence). In Scotland such offences are heard in sheriff courts. A business or individual may be fined for breaking food safety laws. Individuals can also be jailed or prohibited from working with food. Claims for compensation – for instance, when a consumer claims damages after suffering from food poisoning – come under civil law.

The Food Hygiene (England) Regulations, 2006

Food Hygiene (England) Regulations 2006 and equivalent regulations for Wales, Scotland and Northern Ireland came into force in January 2006 replacing many parts of The Food Safety Act 1990. This chapter outlines the main provisions of the Food Hygiene (England) Regulations 2006. It is important to note that this summary is not a complete statement of the law and specialist advice and help may be needed in the workplace.

Structure

The regulations are divided into four parts

1. Preliminary
2. Main provisions
3. Administration and enforcement
4. Miscellaneous and supplementary provisions – with several schedules.

Schedule 4 of these regulations covers temperature control requirements and is also covered in this chapter.

Regulation numbers are quoted here for reference, but it is not necessary to be able to state them.

Part 1 – Preliminary
Regulation 2
Several key words are defined – in particular:

'Authorised officer' means any person who is authorised in writing by the enforcement authority to act in matters arising under the Hygiene Regulations. This would usually be an environmental health practitioner.

'Enforcement authority' is the authority responsible for executing and enforcing the Hygiene Regulations.

'Premises' includes any establishment, any place, vehicle, stall or moveable structure, any ship or aircraft.

Regulation 3
Any food commonly used for human consumption that is found on food premises shall be presumed, until proved to the contrary, to be intended for human consumption.

Part 2 – Main provisions
Regulation 6 – Hygiene improvement notices
If an authorised officer believes that a food business operator is failing to comply with the Hygiene Regulations, a hygiene improvement notice may be served on that person stating:

- what the officer believes is wrong
- why the officer thinks it is wrong
- what should be done to put the problem right
- the time within which the work must be done (not less than 14 days)

It is an offence not to carry out the work within the time specified.

Regulation 7 – Hygiene prohibition orders

If a food business operator is convicted of any offence under relevant regulations and there is a risk to health, a court can be asked to prohibit:

- the use of any process or treatment
- the construction of premises for a food business or the use of equipment in food premises
- work in, or use of, premises or equipment
- the business operator or manager from working in the food business.

A notice – the hygiene prohibition order – has to be conspicuously displayed on the premises as soon as possible and it is an offence to contravene it.

When any of the problems above have been rectified, the local authority must issue a certificate of satisfaction within three days. This allows the premises to re-open. The business operator can apply for this certificate, and the authority must decide within 14 days whether it is satisfied or give the reasons why not.

The court can also impose a prohibition order on the business operator or manager preventing them from working in any food business. In this situation, the business operator can apply to the court to remove the prohibition order from the manager or business operator. Only a court can lift such an order and any application will not be considered for at least six months after the order was made. If the court does not agree to lift the ban, no new application can be made for a further three months.

Regulation 8 – Hygiene emergency prohibition notices and orders

If an authorised officer believes that there is an imminent risk to health, a hygiene emergency prohibition notice can be served. This immediately closes the premises for three days. Within three (working) days of serving the notice, the authorised officer must go to a magistrates' or sheriff court for a hygiene emergency prohibition order to keep the premises closed. Notices and orders must be fixed in a conspicuous position on the premises.

Once the order has been complied with, the business operator must apply for a certificate of satisfaction before the premises can re-open.

If the court decides that there was not an imminent risk to health when the notice was served, or an application for a hygiene emergency prohibition order was not made within three days, the business operator may seek compensation for any loss suffered in complying with the notice.

Regulation 10 – Offences due to another person

Proceedings may also be taken against another person if an offence is due to the act or default of that person.

Regulation 11 – Defence of due diligence

Business operators who can prove that they took all reasonable precautions and exercised all due diligence to avoid the commission of the offence, by himself/herself or by a person under his/her control can call upon the defence of due diligence. To succeed, this defence must establish that the:

- offence was the fault of another person
- the business operator or a trusted person carried out all the necessary checks
- the business operator did not know and had no reason to believe that an act or omission would amount to an offence.

To prove a due diligence defence, evidence must be documented. Evidence may be wide ranging and include records of the following: staff training, hazard analysis systems, temperature checks, cleaning schedules, hygiene audits, customer complaints, maintenance reports, supplier audits, pest control contractor reports.

Part 3 – Administration and enforcement

Regulation 12 – Procurement of samples

Gives authority to an authorised officer to purchase or take samples of any food, food source, contact material or any article or substance that may be required as evidence.

Regulation 13 – Analysis, etc. of samples

Gives authority for any of the samples noted in Regulation 12 to be analysed or examined by a public analyst or food examiner, if required by the authorised officer.

Regulation 14 – Powers of entry

Authorised officers have the right of entry at any reasonable hour both inside and outside the local authority's area. An officer can also obtain a warrant issued by a Justice of the Peace authorising entry if for example, entry has been refused, entry is a matter of urgency, the premises are unoccupied or the owner is temporarily absent. If the building is a private dwelling, 24 hours' notice must be given to the occupier.

Authorised officers must be given access to any records, including computer records and they have the authority to seize and detain any records if they are required as evidence.

Regulation 15 – Obstruction, etc. of officers

It is an offence to obstruct an officer or knowingly to give misleading information.

Regulation 17 – Offences and penalties

A person guilty of an offence under these regulations shall be liable to:

- on summary conviction (at a magistrates' court) to a maximum fine of £5,000
- on conviction on indictment (at a crown court in front of a judge and jury) to imprisonment for up to two years and/or an unlimited fine

A person guilty of obstruction or knowingly giving misleading information on summary conviction can be fined up to £5,000 and/or imprisoned for up to three months.

Regulation 18 – Offences by bodies corporate

Where an offence has been committed by a body corporate (company or organisation) with the consent, connivance of, or due to neglect , by any director, manager, secretary or other similar officer he/she, as well as the body corporate, shall be guilty of that offence.

Regulation 20 – Right of appeal
Regulation 21 – Appeals to crown court

These regulations allow any person who is aggrieved to appeal through either a magistrates' court or a crown court. Appeals against decisions made in a magistrates' court are heard in a crown court.

Regulation 22 – Appeals against hygiene improvement notices and remedial action notices

This regulation allows for appeals against hygiene improvement notices and remedial action notices and for the court to cancel, modify or affirm it.

Regulation 23 – Application of Section 9 of the Food Safety Act, 1990

Section 9 of the Food Safety Act – relating to the inspection and seizure of suspected food – applies to these regulations in relation to an authorised officer of an enforcement authority (see page 155 – under heading Section 9).

Part 4 – Miscellaneous and supplementary provisions

Regulation 27 – Food that has not been produced, processed or distributed in accordance with the Hygiene Regulations

On an inspection of any food, an authorised officer of an enforcement authority may certify that it has not been produced, processed or distributed in compliance with the Hygiene Regulations. In these circumstances it shall be treated as failing to comply with food safety requirements under Section 9 of the Food Safety Act, 1990 (see page 155). Where any food that is certified is part of a batch, all the food within the batch shall be certified – until it is proved that the rest of the food is in compliance with the Hygiene Regulations.

Schedule 4 – Temperature control regulations

The following regulations refer to England, Wales and Northern Ireland.

Regulations for temperature control in Scotland are also covered under Schedule 4 of the regulations, but as these regulations differ from those of England, Wales and Northern Ireland they are dealt with separately (see page 148) .

Chill holding requirements

No one involved in a commercial food operation should keep any food that is likely to support the growth of pathogenic micro-organisms or the formation of toxins at a temperature above 8°C.

Food sent by mail order is exempt, but it must still be sent at a safe temperature.

General exemptions from chill-holding requirements

The chill temperature of 8°C does not apply if food:

- has been cooked or reheated and is for service or is on display for sale and needs to be kept above 63°C to control bacterial growth or the formation of toxins
- can be kept at an ambient temperature with no risk to health for all its shelf life
- has been processed to make it safe – for example, by canning or dehydration
- needs to ripen or mature at an ambient temperature until that process is completed
- is raw and is intended for further processing that will render the food fit for human consumption
- is covered by certain marketing standards – for example, eggs and poultry.

Manufacturers' upward variation of the 8°C limit

There is a defence against holding foods that are likely to support the growth of pathogenic micro-organisms at a temperature above 8°C if the manufacturer, who prepared or processed the food, recommended in writing that the food could be kept at a different temperature for a defined period. However, the manufacturer's recommendation must be backed by well-founded scientific assessment.

Chill-holding tolerance periods

There is a defence for an offence if food:

- was for service or on display for sale
- had not previously been kept for service or display for sale at a temperature above 8°C (or at another recommended temperature)
- had been kept for service or on display for sale for a period of less than four hours
- is being transferred to or from a vehicle that was holding it at below 8°C, or was held above 8°C for an unavoidable reason, for instance:
  - to allow for the practicalities of handling the food during or after processing or preparation
  - during the defrosting of equipment
  - because of a temporary breakdown of equipment and
  - it was for a limited period that was consistent with food safety.

Hot holding

No one should keep food at a temperature below 63°C that has:

- been cooked or reheated
- is for service or on display for sale
- needs to be kept above 63°C to control the growth of pathogenic micro-organisms or the formation of toxins.

Hot holding defences

It is a defence to hold food at below 63°C if:

- scientific assessment concludes that it is safe to hold the food at that temperature for that time
- the food was kept for less than two hours and had not previously been kept for service or on display for sale.

Other temperature requirements for food that is a risk to health

(These are covered under Annex II, Chapter IX of Regulation (EC) No. 852/2004 on the hygiene of foodstuffs, see page 153 – Provisions applicable to foodstuffs). In summary, foodstuffs that are likely to support the growth of pathogenic micro-organisms or the formation of toxins must not be kept at a temperature that would result in a risk to health. Such foods include:

- raw materials
- ingredients
- intermediate products
- finished products.

This section of the regulation also states that:

- if it is consistent with food safety, food can be at a temperature outside the legal control for limited periods to allow for handling during preparation, transport, storage, display and service.
- food should be cooled as quickly as possible after its final heat treatment or final preparation stage.
- during thawing foods must not be subjected to temperatures that would result in a risk to health.

Chill and hot holding requirements in Scotland

Schedule 4 of the Food Hygiene (Scotland) Regulations 2006

Food should be refrigerated, kept in a cool, ventilated place or held at a temperature above 63°C, unless it is:

- being prepared for sale
- displayed for sale or has been sold
- being cooled as quickly as possible under hygienic conditions
- reasonable to store it at a different temperature so that it can be sold
- safe to keep it at ambient temperatures for its stated shelf life.

Reheating food

Food to be reheated for display for sale or immediate consumption must be heated to above 82°C unless this would adversely affect its quality.

Regulation (EC) No. 852/2004 on the hygiene of foodstuffs

This European Union regulation, which applies to all member states, came into force on 1 January 2006 replacing The Food Safety (General Food Hygiene) Regulations, 1995. The majority of the requirements in the new regulations are the same as the ones they replace. The main new requirement (Article 5) involves putting into place a documented food safety management system or procedure based on HACCP principles.

Article 5 – Hazard analysis and critical control points (CCPs)

Food business operators must put in place, implement and maintain permanent procedures based on HACCP principles as follows:

1. Identifying any hazards that must be prevented, eliminated or reduced to acceptable levels.

2. Identifying the critical control points (CCPs) at the steps in the process at which control is essential to prevent or eliminate a hazard or reduce it to acceptable levels.

3. Establishing critical limits at CCPs that identify both what is acceptable and what is unacceptable for the prevention, elimination or reduction of identified hazards.

4. Establishing and putting into place effective monitoring procedures at CCPs.

5. Establishing corrective actions when monitoring indicates that a CCP is not under control.

6. Establishing procedures to verify that measures that have been introduced are working effectively.

7. Establishing documents and records, commensurate with the nature and size of the business, which demonstrate the effective application of the measures that have been introduced.

When any modification is made in the product, process, or any step, the procedure must be reviewed and any necessary changes made to it.

Article 6 – Registration

Food business operators must register each establishment under their control with the local authority. They must also advise of any significant change(s) in activities and any closures of an existing establishment.

Articles 7, 8 and 9 – Guides to good practice

National guides to good practice for hygiene and for the application of HACCP principles shall be developed by food business sectors in consultation with local authorities and consumer groups.

Existing guides (drawn up under Directive 93/43/EEC) shall continue to apply provided that they are compatible with the objectives of this Regulation. The ultimate aim will be to produce Community Guides as identified in Article 9 of the regulations. Although the current *Industry Guides to Good Practice* have no legal force they are generally given due consideration by local authorities when they enforce regulations.

Annex II – General hygiene requirements

Chapter I – General requirements for food premises

Food premises must be kept clean and maintained in good repair and condition.

The layout, design, construction, siting and size of food premises must:

- allow adequate maintenance, cleaning and/or disinfection
- avoid or minimise air-borne contamination
- provide adequate working space to allow for the hygienic performance of all operations
- protect against the accumulation of dirt, contact with toxic materials, shedding of particles into food and the formation of condensation or mould on surfaces
- permit good food hygiene practise, including protection against contamination and, in particular, pest control
- provide, where necessary, suitable temperature-controlled handling and storage conditions to maintain foodstuffs at appropriate temperatures and designed to allow those temperatures to be monitored and, where necessary, recorded

Toilets

There must be an adequate number of flush lavatories available and connected to an effective drainage system. Toilets must not open directly into rooms where food is handled.

Facilities for hand washing

There must be an adequate number of washbasins available, suitably located and used only for cleaning hands.

Washbasins for cleaning must be provided with hot and cold running water, materials for cleaning hands and for hygienic drying.

There must be facilities for washing food that are separate from those for washing hands.

Ventilation

There must be suitable and sufficient means of natural and/or mechanical ventilation. Mechanical airflow from a contaminated area to a clean area must be avoided. Ventilation systems must be constructed to allow filters and other parts requiring cleaning or replacement to be readily accessible.

Toilets must have adequate natural or mechanical ventilation.

Lighting

There must be adequate natural and/or artificial lighting.

Drainage

Drainage facilities must be adequate for the purpose intended.

They must be designed and constructed to avoid the risk of contamination.

Changing facilities

Where necessary, there must be adequate changing facilities provided for staff.

Cleaning agents and disinfectants

Cleaning agents and disinfectants must not be stored in areas where food is handled.

Chapter II – Specific requirements in rooms where foodstuffs are prepared, treated or processed

These regulations exclude dining rooms and moveable and/or temporary premises, such as marquees, market stalls, mobile sales vehicles, premises used primarily as a private dwelling house but where foods are regularly prepared for placing on the market and vending machines.

In rooms where food is prepared, treated and processed the design and layout must permit good hygiene practices, including protection against contamination between and during operations. In particular:

Floors

Floor surfaces must be maintained in a sound condition and be easy to clean and, where necessary, to disinfect.

This will require the use of impervious, non-absorbent, washable and non-toxic materials.

Where appropriate, floors must allow adequate surface drainage.

Walls

Wall surfaces must be maintained in a sound condition and be easy to clean and, where necessary to disinfect.

This will require the use of impervious, non-absorbent, washable and non-toxic materials, and must be smooth up to a height appropriate for the operations.

Ceilings

Ceilings (or, where there are no ceilings, the interior surface of the roof) and any overhead fixtures must be constructed and finished so as to prevent the accumulation of dirt and to reduce condensation, the growth of undesirable mould and the shedding of particles.

Windows

Windows and other openings must be constructed to prevent the accumulation of dirt. Those that can be opened to the outside environment must, where necessary, be fitted with insect-proof screens that can be easily removed for cleaning.

Where open windows would result in contamination, windows must remain closed and fixed when food is being produced.

Doors

Doors must be easy to clean and, where necessary, to disinfect.

This will require the use of smooth and non-absorbent surfaces, unless food business operators can satisfy local authorities that other materials are appropriate.

Surfaces

Surfaces (including surfaces of equipment) in areas where foods are handled and in particular those in contact with food must be maintained in a sound condition and be easy to clean and, where necessary, to disinfect.

This will require the use of smooth, washable, corrosion-resistant and non-toxic materials, unless food business operators can satisfy the local authority that other materials are appropriate.

Facilities for washing equipment and food

Adequate facilities must be provided, where necessary, for cleaning, disinfecting and the storage of working utensils and equipment. These facilities must be constructed of corrosion-resistant materials, be easy to clean and have an adequate supply of hot and cold water.

Adequate provision must be made, where necessary, for washing food. Every sink or such facility provided for the washing of food must have an adequate supply of hot and/or cold potable water and be kept clean and, where necessary, disinfected (see Chapter VII on Water supply on page 153).

Chapter III – Movable and temporary premises (marquees, market stalls, and mobile sales vehicles), vending machines and premises used mainly as a private dwelling house but where foods are regularly prepared to be sold or given to the public

There are different requirements to those already described in Chapters I and II for movable and temporary premises. However, all the requirements of further chapters of the legislation apply.

Premises and vending machines must, as far as is reasonably practicable, be sited, designed, constructed and kept clean and maintained in good repair and condition to avoid the risk of contamination, particularly from animals and pests. In particular, where necessary:

- appropriate facilities must be available to maintain adequate personal hygiene, including facilities for the hygienic washing and drying of hands, hygienic toilet facilities and changing facilities
- surfaces that are in contact with food must be in a sound condition and be easy to clean and, where necessary, to disinfect – this will require the use of smooth, washable, corrosion-resistant and non-toxic materials
- there must be adequate provision for the cleaning and, where necessary, the disinfecting of working utensils and equipment
- where foodstuffs are cleaned as part of the food business' operations, adequate provision must be made to do this hygienically
- an adequate supply of hot and/or cold potable water must be available
- there must be adequate arrangements and/or facilities for the hygienic storage and disposal of hazardous and/or inedible substances and waste (whether liquid or solid)
- there must be adequate facilities and/or arrangements for maintaining and monitoring suitable food temperature conditions
- so far as is reasonably practicable, foodstuffs must be placed in such a way to avoid the risk of contamination.

Chapter IV – Transport

Vehicles and containers used for transporting foodstuffs must be kept clean and maintained in good repair and condition to protect foodstuffs from contamination and, where necessary, designed and constructed to permit adequate cleaning and/or disinfection.

Where necessary, vehicles and containers used for transporting foodstuffs are to be capable of maintaining foodstuffs at appropriate temperatures and allow those temperatures to be monitored.

Chapter V – Equipment requirements

All articles, fittings and equipment that come into contact with food must be:

- effectively cleaned and, where necessary, disinfected – cleaning and disinfection are to take place at a frequency sufficient to avoid any risk of contamination
- constructed, be of such materials and kept in such good order, repair and condition to minimise any risk of contamination and to be kept clean and, where necessary, disinfected
- installed in such a manner to allow adequate cleaning of the equipment and the surrounding area.

Chapter VI – Food waste

Food waste and other refuse must be removed from food rooms as quickly as possible, to avoid it accumulating.

Food waste and other refuse must be deposited in closable containers, which are of appropriate construction, kept in sound condition, be easy to clean and, where necessary, disinfect.

Adequate provision must be made to store and dispose of food waste and other rubbish.

Refuse stores must be designed and managed in such a way to enable them to be kept clean and, where necessary, free of animals and pests.

All food waste must be got rid of in a hygienic and environmentally-friendly way and must not constitute a direct or indirect source of contamination.

Chapter VII – Water supply

There must be an adequate supply of potable water (drinking water) that is to be used, whenever necessary, to ensure that foodstuffs are not contaminated.

Ice that comes into contact with food or that may contaminate food must be made from potable water.

Ice must be made, handled and stored under conditions that protect it from contamination.

Chapter VIII – Personal hygiene

Every person working in a food-handling area must maintain a high degree of personal cleanliness and wear suitable, clean clothing and, where necessary, protective overclothing.

No one suffering from, or who is a carrier of a disease likely to be transmitted through food or afflicted with infected wounds, skin infections, sores or diarrhoea is to be permitted to handle food or enter any food-handling area, in any capacity, if there is any likelihood of direct or indirect contamination.

Any person working in a food business who is affected by any of the above and who is likely to come into contact with food, must report immediately the illness or symptoms and, if possible, their causes to the owner of the business or the manager.

Chapter IX – Provisions applicable to foodstuffs

Raw materials and ingredients must not be accepted if they are known to be, or suspected of being, contaminated and if they would still be unfit after processing.

The storage of raw materials and ingredients must be in appropriate conditions designed to prevent harmful deterioration and protect them from contamination.

Food must be protected from contamination that could make it unfit for human consumption.

Adequate procedures must be in place to control pests and to prevent domestic animals (pets) from having access to areas where food is prepared, handled or stored.

Raw materials, ingredients, intermediate products and finished products likely to support the growth of pathogenic micro-organisms or the formation of toxins must not be kept at temperatures that might result in a risk to health. Limited periods outside temperature control are permitted, to accommodate the practicalities of handling during preparation, transport, storage, display and service of food provided that it does not result in a risk to health. Food businesses manufacturing, handling and wrapping processed foodstuffs are to have suitable rooms, large enough for the separate storage of raw materials from processed material and sufficient separate refrigerated storage.

Where foodstuffs are to be held or served at chilled temperatures they must be cooled as quickly as possible following the heat-processing stage, or final preparation stage if no heat process is applied, to a temperature that does not result in a risk to health.

The thawing of foodstuffs must be undertaken in such a way as to minimise the risk of growth of pathogenic micro-organisms or the formation of toxins in the foods.

Hazardous or inedible substances must be adequately labelled and stored in separate and secure containers.

Chapter X – Provisions applicable to the wrapping and packaging of foodstuffs

Material used for wrapping and packaging must not be a source of contamination.

Wrapping materials must be stored so that they are not exposed to a risk of contamination.

Wrapping and packaging operations must be carried out to avoid contamination of the products. In the case of cans and glass jars, the integrity of the container's construction and its cleanliness must be assured.

Chapter XI – Heat treatment

This regulation applies specifically to foods in hermetically-sealed containers. The process used should conform to an internationally recognised standard (for example, pasteurisation, ultra high temperature or sterilisation). Any heat treatment process must be sufficient to raise every part of the product to a given temperature for a given period of time and to prevent the product from becoming contaminated during the process.

Chapter XII – Training

Food business operators must ensure that:

- food handlers are supervised and instructed and/or trained in food hygiene matters commensurate with their work activity.

- those responsible for the development and maintenance of procedures based on HACCP principles or for the operation of relevant guides have received adequate training in the application of the HACCP principles.

The Food Safety Act, 1990

The Food Hygiene (England) Regulations 2006 and Regulation (EC) No. 852/2004 on the hygiene of foodstuffs replace many of the provisions contained in the Food Safety Act 1990. The relevant sections that still apply are outlined in this chapter.

Section 7

It is an offence to render any food injurious to health with the intention of selling it for human consumption. 'Injurious to health' includes long-term, short-term and cumulative effects and any impairment whether permanent or temporary. An offence may come about by:

- adding any article or substance to a food
- using any article or substance as an ingredient
- abstracting any constituent from the food
- subjecting the food to any process or treatment that renders it injurious to health

Section 9

An authorised officer may, at any reasonable time, inspect food intended for sale for human consumption. If the food fails to satisfy food safety requirements, or is likely to cause food poisoning or any disease communicable to humans, the officer may either:

- give notice that the food must not be used for human consumption but must not be removed or may be removed only to a specified place
- seize it and remove it for a Justice of the Peace (magistrate or sheriff) to deal with.

If the case is taken before a Justice of the Peace (JP), then the person liable to be prosecuted is entitled to speak to the court and to call witnesses. If a notice is withdrawn, or the JP does not condemn the food, the owner is entitled to compensation for any depreciation in its value.

Section 14 – Consumer protection

It is an offence to sell food that is not of the nature, substance or quality demanded by the consumer for example:

- nature – food that is different to that requested
- substance – not of the correct composition or it contains 'foreign bodies'
- quality – if the food has deteriorated.

Other food safety legislation

In addition to the main food safety legislation outlined in the previous chapters, there are additional regulations that you need to be aware of in your role as a supervisor.

Food labelling regulations

The Food Labelling Regulations 1996 require pre-packed food for sale to the ultimate consumer or caterer to be labelled with:

- the name of the food
- a list of ingredients (in descending order of their weight in the finished product)
- an indication of appropriate durability (i.e. a 'best before' date or 'use by' date – see page 61)
- any special storage conditions or conditions of use
- the name and address of the manufacturer, packer or seller
- the place of origin (especially if failure to do so might mislead the purchaser as to the true origin)
- instructions for use (if necessary to make appropriate use of the food).

An amendment to these regulations – The Food Labelling (Amendment) (England) (No. 2) Regulations 2004 (with similar regulations for Wales, Scotland and Northern Ireland) – states that any foods containing allergenic ingredients, or ingredients originating from allergenic ingredients, must be marked or labelled with a clear reference to the name of the allergenic ingredient concerned (see pages 49–50).

Lot marking

To assist in the event of a product recall The Food (Lot Marking) Regulations 1996 require that pre-packed foods be identified with a batch or 'lot' number. The size of a batch and the choice of number are both largely up to the producer, manufacturer, packager or first seller providing the 'lot' number is easily visible, clearly legible and indelible.

Quick-frozen food regulations

The Quick-frozen Food Regulations 1990 and Amendments 1994 affect businesses that produce, store, transport and sell quick-frozen foodstuffs. All businesses have to monitor and record the temperature of the food, which should be kept at or below -18°C. There are certain exemptions for local distributors and retailers. Local distribution vehicles and retail cabinets need to have easily visible thermometers. The temperature must be recorded at frequent, regular intervals and records kept for at least a year. A thermometer is also sufficient for measuring temperatures of food stores in a cold chamber less than 10m3 in a retail premises. For larger cold storage areas in retail premises, or for any means of storage and transport, a system is required that includes instruments for monitoring the air temperature at frequent and regular intervals.

Health and safety at work

Under the Health and Safety at Work etc. Act 1974 employers must ensure, as far as reasonably practicable, the health, safety and welfare of employees. An extensive pest infestation in a food premises may be argued, under this Act, to affect their working conditions.

The Workplace (Health, Safety and Welfare) Regulations 1992 cover aspects of the workplace ranging from ventilation, temperature, lighting, cleaning, maintenance, room dimensions to sanitary facilities. Temperatures in food preparation areas should be reasonable – for example 16°C. If this is not practicable, then adequate methods of cooling should be provided. This provision does not apply to food rooms that have a legal maximum temperature.

Glossary

Acute
The rapid onset of symptoms. For example, illness and the effects of pest bait may be described as acute.

Aerobic
Requiring oxygen. Some bacteria are aerobic and can live only if there is oxygen.

Allergy/allergic reaction
An identifiable immunological response to certain foods or food additives. The symptoms, which vary considerably, can range from mild (for example, tingling or itching in the mouth or a localised rash) to severe (for example, difficulty in breathing or swallowing) through to life-threatening (anaphylactic shock).

Ambient temperature
Strictly speaking, this is the temperature of the surrounding air. However, when talking about food safety, the term is generally used to refer to ordinary room temperature, which is usually within the temperature danger zone.

Anaerobic
Requiring no oxygen. Some bacteria can live only if oxygen is absent.

Anaphylactic shock
A severe allergic reaction to certain foods or food additives. It causes a dramatic fall in blood pressure leading to a rapid loss of consciousness and can be life threatening. Usually treated with an injection of adrenaline, which should be given as soon as possible. It is vital that urgent medical help is sought.

Aseptic
Free from pathogenic micro-organisms.

Authorised officer
An official with legal powers to carry out food safety inspections and to initiate legal action (such as an Environmental Health Practitioner).

a_w
Water activity – the water available to micro-organisms.

Bacteria (singular: bacterium)
Single-celled organisms of various shapes that are visible only through a microscope. Most are harmless and even useful to humans. A small proportion, known as pathogens are harmful, causing food poisoning and other food-borne illnesses.

Bactericide
A chemical that destroys bacteria.

Bacterial food poisoning
An acute disturbance of the gastro-intestinal tract, characterised by abdominal pain, with or without diarrhoea and vomiting, cause by eating food contaminated by pathogenic bacteria or their toxins.

Binary fission
A method of reproduction by division in two. This is the way in which bacteria multiply.

Blanching
Immersion of vegetables into boiling water, or exposure to steam, for a short period before freezing to destroy enzymes and reduce spoilage that may occur during storage (e.g. browning, development of off-flavours, loss of flavour). *See*: enzyme, spoilage.

Blown
A word that describes a can of food that bulges. This is usually caused by gas formation as a result of microbial fermentation (from *Clostridium* species and *Bacillus* species). The contents should not be eaten.

Carrier
Someone infected by a disease-causing organism that does not experience any symptoms but may pass the infection to other people. There are different types of carrier:

Healthy carrier – someone who is infected by a disease-causing organism but who never develops any related symptoms. Such individuals are potentially dangerous as they are usually totally unaware of their condition and as a result are unlikely to pay any extra attention to their personal hygiene.

Incubatory carrier – a person who excretes organisms during the incubation period of a disease and shows no symptoms.

Convalescent carrier – a person who continues to excrete organisms while recovering from a disease and after symptoms have ceased.

Case

Someone with symptoms of a disease who is excreting pathogenic organisms.

Chronic

Something that develops slowly. The symptoms of a chronic disease may appear gradually and last for a prolonged period. Chronic pest bait gradually poisons the pests that consume it over time.

Cleaning

The application of energy to remove soil, food residue, dirt, grease and other objectionable matter.

Colony

A group of bacteria visible without the aid of a microscope.

Contact time

The time required for a disinfectant to reduce pathogenic and spoilage bacteria to a level that is safe for human health

Contamination

The transference of any objectionable or harmful substance or material to food. Contamination may be microbial, physical, chemical or allergenic and may occur directly or by cross-contamination.

Control measure

Any action or activity that can be used to prevent or eliminate a food safety hazard or reduce it to an acceptable level.

Corrective action

Any action to be taken when the results of monitoring at a critical control point (CCP) indicate a loss of control.

Critical control point (CCP)

A step in the process where it is essential to prevent or eliminate a food safety hazard or reduce it to an acceptable level.

Critical limit

A criterion that can be monitored that separates acceptability from unacceptability.

Denature

A process, such as heating, that changes the structure of a protein and may radically affect the texture or taste of a food. The changes in a hen's egg when fried give a good example of the process.

Danger zone

A description of the temperature range 5°C to 63°C that is most suitable for bacterial multiplication. The rate of multiplication varies within the range but in most cases is fastest at 37°C.

Detergent

A chemical, or mixture of chemicals, which help to remove grease, dirt and food particles so that surfaces are prepared for the action of disinfectants.

Disinfectant

A term generally used to describe a chemical used for disinfection. However, disinfection, as detailed below, can also be achieved using hot water and steam as well as chemicals.

Disinfection

The process of reducing pathogenic and spoilage micro-organisms to levels that is safe for human health using chemicals (disinfectants), hot water (over 82°C) or steam.

Endotoxin

A poison produced inside bacteria, generally released on the death and subsequent break up of the cell.

Exotoxin

A poison produced by bacteria that is released outside its body.

Enzyme

Chemicals in the cells of animals, plants and micro-organisms that break down carbon compounds such as proteins, fats and sugars.

Facultative anaerobes

Micro-organisms that can survive with or without the presence of oxygen.

Flow diagram

A systematic representation of the sequence of steps or operations used in the production or manufacture of a particular food item.

Food-borne disease

An illness caused by micro-organisms, such as bacteria and viruses, which use food as a vehicle to move to humans where they can multiply and produce symptoms.

Food-borne illness

The general term for illness linked to food. It covers both food poisoning and food-borne disease.

Food handler

Someone whose work involves food. The term may be used to cover people who work with open food, but is also sometimes extended to cover people whose work could affect the safety of food. Food handlers include production line staff in a food factory, caterers, butchers and shop assistants who deal with food and may also include delivery drivers, waiting staff and ice cream sales staff.

Food hygiene

All the practical measures involved in keeping food safe to eat and wholesome through all stages of handling.

Food poisoning

An acute illness that usually develops rapidly after eating contaminated or poisonous food. The symptoms vary but often include abdominal pain, diarrhoea, vomiting and nausea. May be caused by bacteria and their toxins (also *see* bacterial food poisoning), chemicals, metals, poisonous fish and plants.

Food premises

Any building where food is handled as part of a business, whether for profit or not.

Food safety

The safeguarding (protection or preservation) of food from anything that could harm human health.

Freezer burn

Damage caused to frozen food, usually drying out of the surface during storage when food has been poorly packaged.

Fungus (plural: fungi)

Single-celled micro-organisms including mushrooms, toadstools, moulds and yeasts.

Gastro-enteritis

An inflammation of the stomach and intestines normally causing diarrhoea, stomach pains and nausea and vomiting.

HACCP

HACCP (Hazard Analysis Critical Control Point) is a system that identifies, evaluates, and controls hazards that are significant for food safety.

HACCP plan

A document prepared in accordance with the principles of HACCP to ensure control of hazards that are significant for food safety in a food business.

Hazard

A biological, chemical or physical agent in food, or condition of food, that could cause an adverse health effect (i.e. harm).

Hazard analysis

The process of collecting and evaluating information on hazards and conditions leading to their presence to decide which are significant for food safety and therefore should be addressed in the HACCP plan.

High-risk food

Foods that, under favourable conditions, support the multiplication of pathogenic bacteria and will not receive treatment that would eliminate or reduce the risk of food poisoning before they are consumed. Such foods are usually ready-to-eat, high protein, moist foods that require refrigeration. (Examples include cooked meats, cooked meat products containing gravy and stock, egg products, sandwiches, smoked and cured fish, cream cakes).

Incubation period

The interval between the infection of an individual and the appearance of the first sign or symptom of a disease.

Infective dose

The number of micro-organisms needed to cause illness.

Mesophiles

Organisms that will grow between 10°C and 50°C with an optimum of 35°C. Examples include most common pathogens – *Salmonella*, *Staphylococcus aureus*, *Campylobacter* species.

Micro-organisms

Organisms that are visible only through a microscope. They include yeasts, moulds and bacteria.

Monitor

The act of conducting a planned sequence of observations or measurements of control parameters to assess whether a critical control point (CCP) is under control.

Mould

Various types of microscopic fungus that may appear as woolly patches on food.

Mycotoxin

A toxin produced by some fungi.

Neurotoxin

A toxin that attacks the nervous system.

Obligate aerobes

Organisms that only in the presence of oxygen.

Obligate anaerobes

Organisms that survive only in the absence of oxygen.

Onset period

The period between consumption of contaminated food and the first signs of illness.

Organoleptic

Involving the use of sight, smell, taste, touch and hearing – for example in the inspection of foodstuffs on delivery or before use.

Osmosis

The process by which water moves in and out of cells – a property used in curing / brining where salt chemically combines with water making unavailable to bacteria and moulds therefore preventing spoilage.

Outbreak

Two or more cases of food poisoning or food-borne disease in different families or groups of people.

Oxidation

A chemical reaction involving oxygen that changes the taste and texture of food.

Pathogen

A disease-producing micro-organism – for example *Salmonella* or *Campylobacter*.

Psychrophiles

Organisms that will grow between -5°C and 20°C with an optimum of 10°C. Examples include both bacteria and moulds that cause spoilage in refrigerated foods.

Psychrotrophs

Organisms that will grow between 0°C and 35°C with an optimum of 20°C. They will generally grow readily at refrigeration temperatures and examples include *Listeria monocytogenes* and many spoilage bacteria.

Quarantine

The isolation of raw materials, work in progress or finished products pending an investigation into their acceptability for use, or to ensure that they are not used in error if they have already been rejected.

Sanitiser, sanitizer

A specially formulated chemical that can both clean and disinfect in one operation.

Spoilage

The decomposition of food by bacteria, moulds, enzymes or chemical interactions.

Spore (bacterial)

Some types of bacteria, such as *Clostridium perfringens* and *Bacillus cereus*, have the ability to form spores. They develop inside the vegetative (growing and multiplying) cell to survive adverse conditions such as heat, chemicals, starvation or other threats. Although the original bacterium may die, the spore survives and forms another bacterium when favourable conditions return.

Step

In the context of HACCP – a point, procedure, operation, or stage in the food chain including raw materials, from primary production to final consumption.

Sterilisation

Heat treatment that destroys all living micro-organisms.

Thermophiles

Organisms that will grow between 40°C and 80°C with an optimum of 50°C. Examples include bacteria that cause spoilage in canned foods.

Toxin

Poisons produced by pathogenic bacteria (e.g. *Staphylococcus aureus, Bacillus cereus*) and by other means (e.g. the naturally occurring toxin, haemagglutinin, found in red kidney beans: the toxins produced during storage by mackerel, tuna and sardines that cause Scombrotoxic fish poisoning). The ingestion of toxins in foods is a common cause of food poisoning.

Traceability

The ability to trace or identify batches of raw materials, work in progress or finished products so that, in the event of a failure at a critical control point, they can be identified, isolated and, if necessary, rejected.

Unfit food

Food considered being not suitable for human consumption. Sometimes called spoiled food.

Validation

Obtaining evidence that the elements of the HACCP plan are effective.

Verification

The application of methods, procedures, tests and other evaluations, in addition to monitoring to determine compliance with the HACCP plan.

Verocytotoxin

An especially powerful toxin produced by bacteria such as *Escherichia coli* O157.

Virus

Extremely small pathogens, visible only through an electron microscope that can only multiply in the living cells of a host such as humans.

Water activity (*see* a_w)

The amount of moisture in any food available to bacteria. The a_w of pure water is 1.00. Bacteria prefer an a_w of 0.99.

Wholesome

Food that is safe and palatable to eat.

Yeast

A single-celled fungus that reproduces by budding and grows rapidly on certain foods, especially those containing sugar.

Index

Design: www.red-stone.com
Illustration: Ned Jolliffe
Photography: Andrew Olney

Except pages 5B (Michael Paul/Stockfood Creative/Getty Images), 7T (Eising/Photodisc Green/Getty Images), 7B (John Foxx/Stockbyte Silver/Getty Images), 9T (Maximilian Stock Ltd/Anthony Blake), 10T (Mandy Hartfree-Bright), 10B (John Heseltine/Science Photo Library), 11T (Nick Koudis/Photodisc Green/Getty Images), 11M (Dave King/Dorling Kindersley/Getty Images), 11B (Photodisc/Photodisc Blue/Getty Images), 12T (Tom Schierlitz/The Image Bank/Getty Images), 12B (Larry Dale Gordon/Getty Images), 13T (Graham Day/Anthony Blake), 13M (Joff Lee/Anthony Blake), 13B (Foodcollection/Punchstock), 17L (Science Pictures Ltd/Science Photo Library), 17R (Dr Tony Brain/Science Photo Library), 18 (CNRI/Science Photo Library), 19LT (Foodfolio/Alamy), 19LB (Andrew Twort/Alamy), 19R (Achim Sass/Westend61/ Getty Images), 20T (Stockdisc/Stockdisc Classic/Getty Images), 20M (Jackson Vereen/Cole Group/Photodisc Green/Getty Images), 20B (ImageDJ/Alamy), 23LT (David Scharf/Science Photo Library), 23LM (Dr Gary Gaugler/Science Photo Library), 23LB (CNRI/Science Photo Library), 23RT (David Scharf/Science Photo Library) 23RM (A.B. Dowsett/Science Photo Library), 23RB (Eye of Science/Science Photo Library), 29T (David Scharf/Science Photo Library), 29B (Carlos Davila/Photographer's Choice Rf/Getty Images), 30T (Christina Kennedy/Dk Stock/Getty Images), 30M (Stockdisc/Stockdisc Premium/Getty Images), 30B (Rayes/Digital Vision/Getty Images), 31T (Prof. C.R. Madeley/Science Photo Library), 31B (Science Photo Library), 35LT (Andrew Twort/Alamy), 35LB (Ryan McVay/Photodisc Green/Getty Images), 35R (Foodcollection/Punchstock), 36T (Isabelle Rozenbaum & Frederic Cirou/Photo Alto/Getty Images), 36M (Gerrit Buntrock/Anthony Blake Photo Library), 36B (Anthony Blake/Anthony Blake), 39 (David Muir/Photodisc Red/Getty Images), 40T (Tom Hoenig/ Westend61/Getty Images), 44T (Bill Bachman/Alamy), 44M (Photodisc/Punchstock), 44B (Andy Sotiriou/Photodisc Green/Getty Images), 46T (Image Source/Getty Images), 47 (Mediacolor's/Alamy), 50 (Sparky/The Image Bank/Getty Images), 54T (Eiichi Onodera/Dex Image/Getty Images), 54B (Jo Van Den Berg/Stockfood Creative/Getty Images), 55 (Ryan McVay/Photodisc Red/Getty Images), 56T (Luzia Ellert/Stockfood Creative/Getty Images), 56B (Maximilian Stock Ltd/Anthony Blake Photo Library), 57T (Seelow/Photocuisine/Corbis), 57M (Sian Irvine/Anthony Blake), 57B (Gary Randall/Taxi/Getty Images), 58T (Steve Taylor/Digital Vision/Getty Images), 58M (David Marsden/Anthony Blake Photo Library), 58B (Tim Hill/Anthony Blake Photo Library), 61B (Tony Robins/Anthony Blake), 62LT (Greg Pease/Photographer's Choice/Getty Images), 62LB (John Foxx/Stockbyte Silver/Getty Images), 64 (Tony Robins/Anthony Blake), 67B (Stockbyte Silver/Alamy), 70B (Blend Images/Alamy), 74B (Image Source/Getty Images), 82M (Sunny/Taxi/GettyImages), 85 (Comstock Images/Punchstock), 87T (Image Source/Getty Images), 87M (Erik Von Weber/Stone/Getty Images), 87B (Juniors Bildarchiv/Alamy), 88B (Jann Lipka/ Nordic Photos/Getty Images), 90T (John A Rizzo/Photodisc Green/Getty Images), 93T (Stockdisc/Stockdisc Classic/Getty Images), 93B (ML Harris/Iconica/Getty Images), 95M (Stockbyte Platinum/Alamy), 99B (Image Source/Alamy), 100T (Konrad Zelazowski/Alamy), 100B (Ilene Macdonald/Alamy), 103T (TNTMagazine/Alamy), 103B (Robin Redfern/Ecoscene), 106T (Purestock/Getty Images), 106M (GK Hart/Vikki Hart/Photodisc Red/Getty Images), 106B (Siede Preis/Photodisc Green/Getty Images) 107T (John Edwards/Taxi/Getty Images), 107B (Cyril Laubscher/Dorling Kindersley/ Getty Images), 109T (James Cotier/Stone/Getty Images), 109M (Holt Studios International Ltd/Alamy), 109B (Holt Studios International Ltd/Alamy), 110T (Holt Studios International Ltd/Alamy), 110M (Holt Studios International Ltd/Alamy), 110B (Richard Drury/The Image Bank/Getty Images), 135 (Biotrace International), 136T (Bananastock/Alamy), 139B (Shout/Alamy).

The diagram page 77 was adapted by Food and Drink Federation from Taylor, L. (1978) 'An evaluation of handwashing techniques – 1', *Nursing Times*, 12 January, pp. 54-55 and is reproduced by permission Food and Drink Federation (www.foodlink.org.uk) and Nursing Times and EMAP.

Stock: Era Silk, 50% post-consumer waste and 50% TCF pulp